Klett World Languages

Workbook  1

Contributors

Evelin Alizo

Teresita Barcia

Luis Enrique Elías

Sharon Ferrer

Sonia Josa

Sophie Rouet

Gwenaëlle Rousselet

Linda Villadóniga

Publishers

Florence Pitti

Eduard Sancho

Project Manager

María Jesús Abilleira

Pedagogical Advisors

Florence Pitti

Laia Sant

Editorial Development

Marta Cárdenas

Ana Escourido

Rights Management

María Jesús Abilleira

Design

Jorge Díaz

Alessandro Minoggi

Illustrators

Olga Carmona

Paula Castell

Mar Guixé

Alejandro Milà

Proofreading in English

Mary Lourdes Haedo

Lynne R. Lemley

Su-Yee Lin

Proofreading in Spanish and Linguistic Consultant

Jorge Herrera

Lisset Martínez Herryman

Cover Images Credit

© 2021 Banco de México Diego Rivera Frida Kahlo Museums Trust, Mexico, D.F. / VEGAP; Difusión; Las Fotos Project; mehdi33300, michaeljung, Inside Creative House/iStock

Workbook ISBN: 978-84-18625-33-6

Printed in the EU
2 3 4 5 6 7 8 9 10   29 28 27 26 25 24 23 22

www.klettworldlanguages.com

TABLE OF CONTENTS

¡Empezamos!

1 Look at the pictures.
Whom and what do you recognize?

I recognize...

¡EMPEZAMOS!

SPANISH AROUND THE WORLD

2 **SPANISH LANGUAGE FACTS**

★ **Underline** the correct number for each sentence.

a. Spanish is the **first / second / third** most spoken language in the world.

b. Spanish is the **first / second / third** most studied language in the world.

c. Spanish is the **first / second / third** most studied language in the US.

d. Spanish is the **first / second / third** language most common on the internet.

e. Spanish is the **first / second / third** language on Wikipedia.

f. Spanish is the **first / second / third** language most common on social media.

3 **SPANISH LANGUAGE FACTS**

★★ **Decide** whether the sentences are true (**T**) or false (**F**).
Correct the false sentences.

a. There are almost 500 million Spanish speakers in the world. ☐ T ☐ F

....

b. French is the most used language on the internet. ☐ T ☐ F

....

c. The three most studied languages in the world are: English, Chinese, and Spanish. ☐ T ☐ F

....

d. Spain is the country with the largest number of Spanish speakers. ☐ T ☐ F

....

4 **SPANISH LANGUAGE FACTS**

★★ **Do** some research on the Spanish language.
Write down three interesting facts.

....

....

....

SPANISH IN THE UNITED STATES

¡EMPEZAMOS!

5 **SPANISH LANGUAGE FACTS**
★★ **Answer** the questions below in English.

a. What are the two most-spoken languages in the US?

....

b. How many people in the US have Hispanic orgin?

....

c. Can you name three US states with names that originated from the Spanish language?

....

d. Can you name five US cities with names that originated from the Spanish language?

....

6 **SPANISH WORDS USED IN ENGLISH**
★ **Look at** the word cloud.
Which words do you recognize? Which ones do you use in English?

MAESTRO
AFICIONADO SUAVE FIESTA
SIESTA
SUAVE PATIO EMBARGO BRONCO TACO
PLAZA SOLO
AFICIONADO
BODEGA BARRIO GRATIS POLITICO RODEO
MOSQUITO PRONTO PRONTO EMBARGO
PLAZA MESA AFICIONADO SUAVE BODEGA
FIESTA SOLO BURRITO MAESTRO AMIGO SIESTA
HACIENDA FIESTA CAFETERIA
MAESTRO CAFETERIA MOSQUITO PATIO
PRONTO RODEO
AFICIONADO SUAVE PLAZA
CAFETERIA
MESA CAFETERIA FIESTA GRATIS
TACO
BRONCO AFICIONADO AMIGO
AMIGO FIESTA BURRO MOSQUITO SUAVE
BARRIO SIESTA
SIESTA FIESTA
HACIENDA RODEO
TANGO MESA

....
....
....

HISTORY OF THE SPANISH LANGUAGE

7 HISTORY OF THE SPANISH LANGUAGE

★ **Take** the test.

1. The Roman Empire conquered modern Spain in the...

a. 3ʳᵈ century BC. ☐

b. 10ᵗʰ century. ☐

c. 15ᵗʰ century. ☐

2. Latin...

a. was mixed with native languages. ☐

b. wasn't mixed with native languages. ☐

3. Romance languages are...

a. the languages derived from other European languages. ☐

b. the languages derived from Latin. ☐

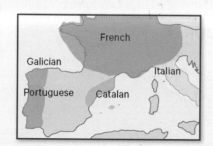

4. Spanish conquistadores brought the Spanish language to the Americas in the...

a. 3ʳᵈ century BC. ☐

b. 10ᵗʰ century. ☐

c. 15ᵗʰ century. ☐

5. California, Nevada, Colorado, and Florida...

a. are names given by English colonists. ☐

b. are names given by Spanish *conquistadores*. ☐

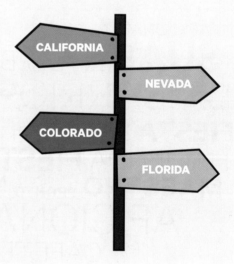

6. Spanish speakers...

a. find it easy to understand each other. ☐

b. find it difficult to understand each other. ☐

HOLA, ¿QUÉ TAL?

¡EMPEZAMOS!

8 LOS SALUDOS • LAS DESPEDIDAS

★ **Look at** the pictures.
Underline the correct term to show if each one is **un saludo** or **una despedida**.

saludo / despedida   **saludo / despedida**   **saludo / despedida**

9 LOS SALUDOS • LAS DESPEDIDAS

★★ **Look at** the pictures.
Write a dialogue for each one.

LETRAS Y SONIDOS

¡EMPEZAMOS!

10 EL ALFABETO Y LOS SONIDOS

★ **A. Write** the name of the letters of these words: **español** and **Montana**.

E, e	.......la e.......	**M, m**	....
S, s	....	**O, o**	....
P, p	....	**N, n**	....
A, a	....	**T, t**	....
Ñ, ñ	....	**A, a**	....
O, o	....	**N, n**	....
L, l	....	**A, a**	....

B. Spell your first and last name, using the full name of the Spanish letters.
Example: ABEL: la a - la be - la e - la ele.

....
....

11 EL ALFABETO Y LOS SONIDOS

★★ **Look at** the highlighted letters in orange.

🔊 **Listen to** the words and **circle** the correct answer.

a. It sounds similar to *h* in *hut.* → **g**ato   **j**aguar   **h**elado

b. It sounds like *a* in *avocado.* → **a**beja   **e**lefante   **i**sla

c. It sounds like *oo* in *food.* → **u**va   **o**so   **a**beja

12 EL ALFABETO Y LOS SONIDOS

★★ **Look at** the highlighted letters in orange.

🔊 **Listen to** the words and **circle** the one with a different pronunciation.

a. **r**ana   pe**rr**o   Pe**r**ú   son**r**isa

b. **c**ereza   **c**o**c**o   que**s**o   **c**asa

c. **g**ato   hambur**g**uesa   **g**irasol   **g**uitarra

d. **g**irasol   **g**eografía   **g**ol   **j**aguar

Copyright © by Difusión, S. L.

LETRAS Y SONIDOS

13 UNA LETRA, DOS SONIDOS

★★ **A. Listen to** the pronunciation of the words below.

🔊 **Look at** the highlighted letters in orange.
Are they pronounced the same? Yes | No

1. casa	**4.** coco	**7.** equis
2. queso	**5.** quesadilla	**8.** doce
3. cine	**6.** cereza	**9.** cuadro

B. Underline the correct option for each sentence.

1. **C** + **a**, **o**, **u** sounds **like *c* in *cool*** / **like *c* in *Cecily***.

2. **C** + **e**, **i** sounds **like *c* in *cool*** / **like *c* in *Cecily***.

3. **QU** + **e**, **i** sounds **like *c* in *cool*** / **like *c* in *Cecily***.

14 UNA LETRA, DOS SONIDOS

★★ **A. Listen to** the pronunciation of the words below.

🔊 **Look at** the highlighted letters in orange.
Are they pronounced the same? Yes | No

1. gente	**4.** gorila	**7.** gas
2. guante	**5.** guía	**8.** hamburguesa
3. gato	**6.** girasol	**9.** goma

B. Underline the correct option for each sentence.

1. **G** + **a**, **o**, **u** sounds **like *g* in *game*** / **similar to *h* in *hut***.

2. **G** + **e**, **i** sounds **like *g* in *game*** / **similar to *h* in *hut***.

3. **GU** + **e**, **i** sounds **like *g* in *game*** / **similar to *h* in *hut***.

15 UNA LETRA, DOS SONIDOS

★★ **Listen to** the pronunciation of the words below.

🔊 **Look at** the highlighted consonants and **say** if they sound strong or soft.

a. ratón Strong | Soft   **d.** príncipe Strong | Soft

b. Honduras Strong | Soft   **e.** perro Strong | Soft

c. Ramón Strong | Soft   **f.** Nicaragua Strong | Soft

¿DE DÓNDE ERES?

¡EMPEZAMOS!

16 LOS PAÍSES HISPANOHABLANTES

★ Where are our **reporteros** from?
Write the names of their countries on the map.

Soy Dana. Soy de los Estados Unidos.

Soy Guada. Soy de México.

Soy Laura. Soy de España.

Soy Andrés. Soy del Perú.

a

Soy Sebastián. Soy de Puerto Rico.

b

c

Soy Juan José. Soy de Colombia.

d

e

f

1. ....

5. ....

2. ....

3. ....

4. ....

6. ....

Copyright © by Difusión, S. L.

¿QUÉ DÍA ES HOY?

17 **LOS DÍAS DE LA SEMANA**

★ **A. Put** these days of the week **in order**.

 martes ☐   viernes ☐   lunes 1

sábado ☐   miércoles ☐   jueves ☐

B. What days do you have Spanish class?

....

18 **LOS MESES**

★ **Complete** the calendars with the names of the months.

.... enero ....

Enero						
L	M	M	J	V	S	D
	1	2	3	4	5
6	7	8	9	10	11	12
13	14	15	16	17	18	19
20	21	22	23	24	25	26
27	28	29	30	31		

....						
L	M	M	J	V	S	D
					1	2
3	4	5	6	7	8	9
10	11	12	13	14	15	16
17	18	19	20	21	22	23
24	25	26	27	28	29	

....						
L	M	M	J	V	S	D
						1
2	3	4	5	6	7	8
9	10	11	12	13	14	15
16	17	18	19	20	21	22
23	24	25	26	27	28	29
30	31					

abril						
L	M	M	J	V	S	D
	1	2	3	4	5
6	7	8	9	10	11	12
13	14	15	16	17	18	19
20	21	22	23	24	25	26
27	28	29	30			

....						
L	M	M	J	V	S	D
			1	2	3
4	5	6	7	8	9	10
11	12	13	14	15	16	17
18	19	20	21	22	23	24
25	26	27	28	29	30	31

junio						
L	M	M	J	V	S	D
1	2	3	4	5	6	7
8	9	10	11	12	13	14
15	16	17	18	19	20	21
22	23	24	25	26	27	28
29	30					

....						
L	M	M	J	V	S	D
		1	2	3	4	5
6	7	8	9	10	11	12
13	14	15	16	17	18	19
20	21	22	23	24	25	26
27	28	29	30	31		

....						
L	M	M	J	V	S	D
					1	2
3	4	5	6	7	8	9
10	11	12	13	14	15	16
17	18	19	20	21	22	23
24	25	26	27	28	29	30
31						

‹ septiembre ›						
L	M	M	J	V	S	D
	1	2	3	4	5	6
7	8	9	10	11	12	13
14	15	16	17	18	19	20
21	22	23	24	25	26	27
28	29	30				

....						
L	M	M	J	V	S	D
			1	2	3	4
5	6	7	8	9	10	11
12	13	14	15	16	17	18
19	20	21	22	23	24	25
26	27	28	29	30	31	

‹ noviembre ›						
L	M	M	J	V	S	D
						1
2	3	4	5	6	7	8
9	10	11	12	13	14	15
16	17	18	19	20	21	22
23	24	25	26	27	28	29
30						

....						
L	M	M	J	V	S	D
	1	2	3	4	5	6
7	8	9	10	11	12	13
14	15	16	17	18	19	20
21	22	23	24	25	26	27
28	29	30	31			

¿QUÉ DÍA ES HOY?

¡EMPEZAMOS!

19 LOS NÚMEROS
★★ **Solve** the following math problems.
Spell out the numbers.

a. **3** x ___dos___ = **seis**

b. **10** + _____ = **quince**

c. **6** + _____ = **nueve**

d. **10** – _____ = **dos**

e. _____ **+ UNO = catorce**

f. **CINCO x TRES =** _____

g. **veinte + 8 =** _____

h. _____ **– ocho = dos**

i. _____ **+ tres = veinte**

j. _____ **– cinco = veinticinco**

20 LAS FECHAS
★★ When do these celebrations take place?
Write the dates in Spanish.
Spell out the numbers.

a. Inauguration Day

Veinte de enero

b. Valentine's Day

c. St. Patricks' Day

d. Independence Day

e. Halloween

f. Veterans Day

¿QUÉ TIEMPO HACE?

21 **¿QUÉ TIEMPO HACE?**
★★ What is the weather like in these Latin American countries?

a. En México ~~está despejado.~~

b. En Cuba ....

c. En Venezuela ....

d. En Colombia ....

e. En Perú ....

f. En Bolivia ....

g. En Argentina ....

h. En Chile ....

¿QUÉ TIEMPO HACE?

22 LAS ESTACIONES

★ **Look at** the picture.
Write the names of each season.

a. ....

b. ....

d. ....

c. ....

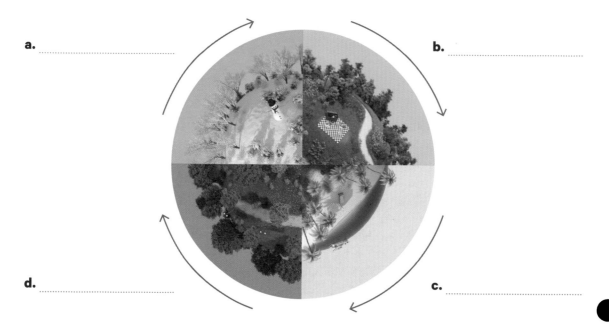

23 LAS ESTACIONES • LOS HEMISFERIOS

★★ **Look at** the chart.
What season is it on these dates in Mexico (Northern Hemisphere)
and in Argentina (Southern Hemisphere)?

	MÉXICO	ARGENTINA
a. Hoy es 26 de julio.	Es verano.	
b. Hoy es 6 de enero.		
c. Hoy es 19 de abril.		
d. Hoy es 23 de marzo.		
e. Hoy es 2 de febrero.		
f. Hoy es 30 de septiembre.		

EN EL SALÓN DE CLASE

24 **EN EL SALÓN DE CLASE**

★ A student needs to buy the following classroom objects.
Complete the list.

(a)

(b)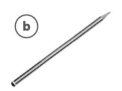

(c)

(d)

(e)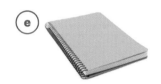

(f)

(g)

(h)

a. un estuche ....

b. ....

c. ....

d. ....

e. ....

f. ....

g. ....

h. ....

25 **EN EL SALÓN DE CLASE**

★★ **Find** seven words associated with school in the word search.
Write them next to the corresponding picture.

T	M	E	S	A	N	R	A	C	N	R	E
S	R	A	A	O	V	E	N	O	U	E	P
I	U	P	I	Z	A	R	R	Ó	N	L	U
L	E	V	I	I	A	A	O	A	A	O	E
L	M	N	H	H	D	J	R	O	O	J	R
A	J	U	C	C	E	R	N	L	O	E	T
L	X	U	O	O	V	E	N	T	A	N	A
P	A	P	E	L	E	R	A	R	E	A	O

a. mesa ....

b. ....

c. ....

d. ....

e. ....

f. ....

g. ....

¿PUEDE REPETIR, POR FAVOR?

¡EMPEZAMOS!

26 **¿PUEDE REPETIR, POR FAVOR?**
★★ **Complete** the dialogues with the correct expressions.

¿Cómo se dice "notebook" en español?   De nada.   ¿Puedo ir al baño?

Lo siento.   ¿Puedes repetir, por favor?   ¿Cómo se deletrea?

a

● ¡Muchas gracias!

o De nada.

b

● ....

o Sí, la fiesta es el 2 de febrero.

c

● ....

o Erre, a, eme, o, ene.

d

● ....

o Se dice "cuaderno".

e

● ....

o Sí.

f

● ....

RAZONES PARA APRENDER ESPAÑOL

27 **RAZONES PARA APRENDER ESPAÑOL**

★ **Read** about some reasons for learning Spanish.
What are your reasons for learning it?
Write them below in English.

viajar a un país
hispanohablante.
*travel to a Spanish-
speaking country.*

**YOU WILL
NEED SPANISH
IF YOU WANT
TO...**

vivir en un país
hispanohablante.
*live in a Spanish-
speaking country.*

estudiar en un país
hispanohablante.
*study in a Spanish-
speaking country.*

interactuar con
hispanohablantes
en los Estados Unidos.
*interact with Spanish
speakers in the US.*

aprender sobre
las culturas de los países
hispanohablantes.
*learn about the cultures
of Spanish-speaking
countries.*

CALENDARIO CULTURAL

¡EMPEZAMOS!

28 **CALENDARIO CULTURAL**

★ **Take** the test.

1. Día de Reyes is celebrated in...

a. Puerto Rico only. ☐

b. many Latin American countries. ☐

2. Carnaval de Barranquilla takes place...

a. on a fixed day in March. ☐

b. either in February or in March. ☐

3. In the Andean culture, Inti is...

a. the sun god. ☐

b. the rain god. ☐

4. Simón Bolívar was a...

a. Spanish *conquistador*. ☐

b. Venezuelan political leader. ☐

5. Grito de Dolores takes place in...

a. September. ☐

b. October. ☐

c. November. ☐

6. Día de Muertos is celebrated in...

a. Mexico only. ☐

b. many Latin American countries. ☐

UNIDAD
1
Soy de los Estados Unidos

1 **A. Watch** the video.

Fill in the chart below with information about Dana.

NAME	AGE	CITY

COUNTRY	LANGUAGES	OTHER INFORMATION

B. Watch the video again and **verify** your answers.

Hola, soy Dana

MI VOCABULARIO

UNIDAD 1

2 LA CORTESÍA • LOS TÍTULOS

★ **Read** the dialogues. Are they formal or informal?
Underline the correct answer for each dialogue.

🔊

a Es un diálogo **formal** / **informal**.

- Emilio, ¿eres de Colombia?
- No, yo soy de Cuba. ¿Y tú?
- Yo soy de México.

b Es un diálogo **formal** / **informal**.

- ¡Hola! ¿Qué tal? Yo soy María. ¿Y tú?
- Yo soy Lara. Encantada.

c Es un diálogo **formal** / **informal**.

- Buenos días, doña Lupita, ¿cómo está?
- Bien, bien, gracias.

d Es un diálogo **formal** / **informal**.

- ¿Son ustedes de la escuela?
- Sí, somos estudiantes. ¿Y tú?
- Yo también soy estudiante.

e Es un diálogo **formal** / **informal**.

- Buenos días. ¿Es usted el señor Álvarez?
- Sí, soy el profesor de español.

f Es un diálogo **formal** / **informal**.

- Buenos días. ¿Son ustedes profesores de esta escuela?
- Sí. ¿Es usted la señora Ortiz?
- Sí, soy yo.

Hola, soy Dana

MI VOCABULARIO

3 **LOS SALUDOS • LAS DESPEDIDAS**

★★ **Complete** the dialogues with the words below.

Buenos días   Encantada.   ¡Hasta pronto!

eres   soy   Bien, gracias.   ¿Qué tal?

a. • ¡Hola! ¿Qué tal? ....

o Bien, ¿y tú?

• ....

b. • Adiós, Manu, ¡nos vemos!

o ¡Adiós! ....

c. • ...., ¿ .... Mariana?

o Sí, ... Mariana. ¿Y tú?

• Yo soy Lucía. ....

o Mucho gusto.

4 **LOS SALUDOS • LAS DESPEDIDAS**

★ **Write** the expressions on the right under the correct picture.

un abrazo

un beso

un apretón de manos

saludar

Hola, soy Dana  LECCIÓN 1

MI GRAMÁTICA

5 SUBJECT **PRONOUNS**

★ **Match** the beginnings of the sentences (**a–f**) with the correct endings (**1–6**).

a. Yo

b. Vosotros

c. Ustedes

d. Tú

e. Usted

f. Nosotros

1. son profesoras del colegio.

2. somos estudiantes.

3. es el profesor de Español.

4. soy de los Estados Unidos.

5. sois de Canadá.

6. eres de Venezuela.

> **ESTRATEGIA**
>
> **Make your own charts**
>
> To better memorize personal pronouns, you can **create a chart or an outline with colors and hang it** in a visible place in your study space.

6 SUBJECT **PRONOUNS**

★★ **Underline** the correct pronoun for each verb.

a. ● ¿Es **ella / usted / tú** la profesora de español?

○ Sí, soy yo.

b. ● ¿Eres **ella / usted / tú** la portavoz del colegio *(school's spokesperson)*?

○ Sí, soy yo.

c. Ellos / Ustedes / Nosotros somos estudiantes.

d. ● ¿Son **ellos / ustedes / nosotros** de los Estados Unidos?

○ No, somos del Ecuador.

e. ● ¿Son **ellos / ustedes / nosotros** de los Estados Unidos?

○ Sí, Joe es de Chicago y Sarah, de Nueva York.

7 SER

★★ **Complete** the sentences with the correct form of **ser**.

a. ● Marta y yo ...... somos ...... de Puerto Rico.

Y ustedes, ¿de dónde .... ?

○ Yo .... de Colombia
y ella .... de Venezuela.

b. ● Y tú, ¿de dónde .... ?

○ Yo .... del Perú.

● Luis y Miguel ....
también del Perú.

Se llama Ángela

MI VOCABULARIO

8 **LOS DATOS PERSONALES (1)**

★ **Read** the information about these three **reporteros**.
Complete the chart below.

a
- Dana
- 15 de agosto
- Hernández
- DG14@mail.difu
- Estados Unidos

b
- Martínez
- Puerto Rico
- soysebas@mail.difu
- Sebastián
- 26 de diciembre

c
- México
- Guadalupe
- guada06@mail.difu
- 11 de junio
- Gómez

	a	b	c
Nombre	Dana		
Apellido			
Cumpleaños			
País			
Correo electrónico			

Se llama Ángela

MI VOCABULARIO

UNIDAD 1

9 LOS DATOS PERSONALES (1)

★ **A. Complete** Dana's presentation with the information from activity 8.

Se llama __Dana Hernández.__ ....

Su cumpleaños es el ....

Es de ....

Su correo electrónico es ....

B. Write complete sentences to introduce Sebastián and Guadalupe.
Use the information from activity 8.

Se llama Ángela

MI GRAMÁTICA

10 DEFINITE ARTICLES

★ Singular or plural? **Put a mark** (✓) in the correct column.

	SINGULAR	PLURAL
a. la papelera		
b. los papeles		
c. el pizarrón		
d. las computadoras		

11 DEFINITE ARTICLES

★★ **Complete** the sentences using **el**, **la**, **los**, or **las**.

a. Olivia es ....la.... compañera de Dana.

b. Mi cumpleaños es .... dos de enero.

c. .... canciones de ChocQuibTown

son increíbles.

d. Yo soy de .... Estados Unidos.

e. .... apellidos de Eva son López Lama.

f. ¿Cómo se llama .... muchacha

de la foto?

g. .... deportes favoritos de Teresa

son el tenis y la gimnasia.

12 LLAMARSE

★ **Fill in** the blanks with the correct reflexive pronoun.

a. ....Me.... llamo Noemí.

b. ¿Cómo .... llaman ustedes?

c. .... llamamos Ángel y Sara.

d. ¿Cómo .... llamas?

e. Ella .... llama Antonia.

f. Ellos .... llaman Leo y Sue.

g. ¿............... llama usted Frank Taylor?

h. La profesora .... llama Gloria.

13 LLAMARSE

★★ **Complete** the dialogues with the correct form of **llamarse**.

a. ● Hola, yo ....me llamo.... Susana.

Y ustedes, ¿cómo ....?

○ .... Raúl y África.

b. ● ¿Cómo .... tu papá?

○ .... Ernesto de Diego.

c. ● ¿Cómo .... tú?

○ .... Andrés.

d. ● Nosotros .... Miguel y Sara.

Y usted, ¿cómo ....?

○ .... Asunción.

¿Cuántos años tienes?

MI VOCABULARIO

UNIDAD 1

14 LOS NÚMEROS (1) • LOS DATOS PERSONALES (2)
★ **Listen to** the conversation and **write** the telephone number of each person.

Nombre: **Maya Elisa Rodríguez**
Teléfono: 555 ....

Nombre: **Reynaldo Torres**
Teléfono: ....

Nombre: **Evelyn Perea**
Teléfono: ....

Nombre: **Ricardo José Alonso**
Teléfono: ....

15 LOS NÚMEROS (1)
★★ **Solve** the riddles. The answers must be numbers from 1 to 31.
Spell out the numbers.

> Tenemos un 3.
> ¿Qué números somos?

a. Somos el _tres_ , el _trece_ , el .... ,
el ....
y el ....

> Tenemos un 4.
> ¿Qué números somos?

b. Somos el .... ,
el ....
y el ....

> Tenemos un 5.
> ¿Qué números somos?

c. Somos el .... ,
el ....
y el ....

> Tenemos un 8.
> ¿Qué números somos?

d. Somos el .... ,
el ....
y el ....

¿Cuántos años tienes? ████████████████████████████████ LECCIÓN 1

MI VOCABULARIO

16 RECUERDA: LOS MESES

★ **Complete** the series with the missing month.

a. enero ......febrero...... marzo

b. .... septiembre octubre

c. abril mayo ....

d. septiembre octubre ....

e. junio .... agosto

f. noviembre .... enero

17 LOS NÚMEROS (1) • RECUERDA: LOS MESES

★★ **Read** Dana's birthday list.
Write her friends' birthdays.
Spell out the numbers.
Remember that in Spanish, dates are written in this order: day / month.

CUMPLEAÑOS

06/01: Carlos	16/08: Beatriz
13/03: María	28/10: Luis
23/06: José	31/12: Mili

a. El cumpleaños de Carlos es el seis de enero. ....

b. El cumpleaños de María es ....

c. El cumpleaños de José es ....

d. El cumpleaños de Beatriz es ....

e. El cumpleaños de Luis es ....

f. El cumpleaños de Mili es ....

18 LOS NÚMEROS (1) • RECUERDA: LOS MESES

★★ When are these holidays celebrated? **Spell out** the numbers.

a. San Valentín es ....

b. El Día de la Independencia es ....

c. Halloween es ....

d. Fin de Año es ....

¿Cuántos años tienes?

MI GRAMÁTICA

19 **TENER** (IE) • **RECUERDA:** **SER** • **RECUERDA:** **LLAMARSE**

★★ **Complete** the sentences with the correct forms of the verbs in parentheses.

a. Mis papás **(ser)** ..... son ..... colombianos.

b. Mi mamá y yo **(llamarse)** .... igual (*the same*): Sofía.

c. Pablo y tú **(ser)** .... de España, ¿no?

d. Yo **(tener)** .... 15 años.

e. Marta no **(tener)** .... correo electrónico.

f. Anne, ¿**(ser, tú)** .... estadouniense o colombiana?

20 **TENER** (IE) • **RECUERDA:** **SER** • **RECUERDA:** **LLAMARSE**

★★★ **Underline** the correct answer in these two dialogues between students.

a. ● Hola, ¿cómo **te llamas** / **nos llamamos**?

  ○ **Se llama** / **Me llamo** Fede. ¿Y tú?

  ● Diego. Yo **eres** / **soy** de Colombia.
   Y tú, ¿de dónde **eres** / **es**?

  ○ Yo, de Chile.

b. ● Hola, ¿**es** / **son** estudiantes del 9.º grado?

  ○ Sí, **somos** / **sois** del 9.º grado. ¿Y tú?

  ● Yo **sois** / **soy** del 10.º grado. Y ustedes,
   ¿cuántos años **tienes** / **tienen**?

  ○ Yo **tenemos** / **tengo** 14 años
   y ella **tiene** / **tengo** 15.

21 **QUESTION WORDS**

★ **Complete** the conversation with the missing word(s).

● ¿^a ..... Cómo ..... te llamas?

○ Me llamo Lorena.

● ¿^b .... eres?

○ Soy de Perú.

● ¿^c .... años tienes?

○ Tengo 17 años.

● ¿^d .... es tu cumpleaños?

○ El 14 de junio.

● ¿^e .... es tu número de teléfono?

○ Es el (555) 703-836.

Soy fan de...

MI VOCABULARIO

22 **LAS OCUPACIONES**

★ **Cross out** two letters to **find out** what these famous people do for a living, then **write** it below.

Gustavo Dudamel

A	D	I	E	R	E	C	T	O	R

el director

Gina Rodríguez

A	C	T	R	E	I	S	Z

la ....

Mitsuharu Tsumura

C	O	U	C	I	N	I	E	R	O

el ....

Serena Auñón-Chancellor

A	S	T	O	R	O	N	A	U	T	E	A

la ....

Jorge Ramos

P	J	E	R	I	R	O	D	I	S	T	A

el ....

Sarah Robles

D	E	P	E	O	R	T	E	I	S	T	A

la ....

23 **LOS NÚMEROS (2)**

★★ **Listen to** the numbers spoken.

🔊 **Spell out** the numbers.

a. ....

b. ....

c. ....

d. ....

24 **LOS NÚMEROS (2)**

★★★ **Spell out** the numbers.

a. **33** treinta y tres ....

b. **46** ....

c. **59** ....

d. **60** ....

e. **66** ....

f. **72** ....

g. **97** ....

h. **100** ....

UNIDAD 1

Soy fan de...

MI VOCABULARIO

UNIDAD 1

25 **LAS OCUPACIONES • LOS NÚMEROS (1 Y 2) • RECUERDA: LOS MESES**

★★ **Look at** the pictures and the information given on the card for each person.
Complete the cards with each person's date of birth, age, and occupation.
Spell out any numbers or dates.

ELIZABETH ACEVEDO
15/02/1988

Su cumpleaños es el _quince de febrero._

Tiene _____

Es _____

ENRIQUE IGLESIAS
08/05/1975

Su cumpleaños es el _____

Tiene _____

Es _____

DIANA TAURASI
11/06/1982

Su cumpleaños es el _____

Tiene _____

Es _____

JOSEPH JULIAN SORIA
28/08/1986

Su cumpleaños es el _____

Tiene _____

Es _____

Soy fan de...

MI GRAMÁTICA

26 **GENDER AND NUMBER OF NOUNS (1 Y 2)**

★ **Put a mark** (✓) in the correct column. Then **write** the masculine or feminine form.

	MASCULINE	FEMININE
a. el profesor	✓	la profesora
b. la estudiante		
c. la jueza		
d. la deportista		
e. el cocinero		

27 **GENDER AND NUMBER OF NOUNS (1 Y 2)**

★★ **Select** the correct answer(s).

a. Son cocineros de un restaurante.
  1. Gustavo y Miguel ☐
  2. Ana y Sofía ☐
  3. Gustavo y Ana ☐

b. Son actrices de Hollywood.
  1. Fernando y Alberto ☐
  2. Esther y Sonia ☐
  3. Fernando y Esther ☐

c. Son directoras de cine.
  1. Daniel y Enrique ☐
  2. Sara y Diana ☐
  3. Enrique y Diana ☐

d. Son periodistas de la CNN.
  1. Jorge y Antonio ☐
  2. Pamela y Elena ☐
  3. Jorge y Elena ☐

28 **GENDER AND NUMBER OF NOUNS (1 Y 2)**

★★★ **Fill in** the blanks with the correct ending of the noun.

a. Tengo dos libros de Elizabeth Azevedo.

b. Pau y Marc Gasol son dos deportist........ .

c. Ferran Adrià es un cociner........ español.

d. Lisa y Pamela son dos compañer........ de clase.

e. Las ciudad........ de Nueva York y Los Ángeles tienen muchos habitantes hispanos.

f. En mi familia tenemos dos computador........ .

g. Dana es fan de diferentes artist........ .

Comunicación

INTERPRETIVE

1 INTERPRETIVE READING

Below, you will find Laura Aguirre's belongings.
You will use them to answer the questions that follow.

UNIDAD 1

LECCIÓN 1

(Before reading)

A. Look at Laura's documents and notes on the previous page.
Write the letter of the corresponding picture next to the type of document.

1. Social network [a]   **3.** Calendar [ ]   **5.** Cell phone case [ ]

2. Business card [ ]   **4.** Photo album [ ]   **6.** Post-it note [ ]

(First reading)

B. Answer the following questions about Laura.

1. ¿Cuál es el apellido de Laura?   El apellido de Laura es Aguirre.

2. ¿De dónde es? ....

3. ¿Cuántos años tiene? ....

4. ¿Cuándo es su cumpleaños? ....

5. ¿Cuál es su ocupación? ....

(Second reading)

C. Decide whether the sentences below are true (**T**) or false (**F**).
Correct the false sentences.

1. El papá de Laura es de México y su mamá es de los Estados Unidos. [T] [F]

....

2. El cumpleaños de Laura es en verano *(summer)*. [T] [F]

....

3. El cumpleaños de la mamá de Laura es el miércoles, ocho de enero. [T] [F]

....

4. Laura tiene cincuenta y seis amigos en su red social favorita. [T] [F]

....

5. El número de teléfono del papá de Laura acaba *(ends)* en veinticinco. [T] [F]

....

Comunicación

INTERPRETIVE

2 INTERPRETIVE LISTENING
You are going to listen to a conversation between Angélica, a new student, and a clerk in the school's office.

(Before listening)

A. Look at this student's card before listening to the conversation.
This will help you focus on key information.

DATOS DEL / DE LA ESTUDIANTE

Apellido: Sánchez

Nombre: Angélica

Edad:

Cumpleaños:

País de origen:

Teléfono: No ☐ **/ Sí** ☐ ....

Correo electrónico: No ☐ **/ Sí** ☐ ....

DATOS DEL / DE LA RESPONSABLE (papá, mamá o tutor / tutora legal)

Apellido:

Nombre:

País de origen:

Ocupación:

Teléfono: No ☐ **/ Sí** ☐ ....

Correo electrónico: No ☐ **/ Sí** ☐ ....

🔊 (First listen)

B. Fill in the student's card according to the information you heard.
Remember: **Listen for** key words. It is not necessary to understand every word.

🔊 (Second listen)

C. Focus on the information that you didn't catch the first time.
You should have a better idea of where in the conversation you will find the missing information.

Comunicación

PRESENTATIONAL

3 **PRESENTATIONAL WRITING**

You are going to write a short paragragh for a Hispanic magazine introducing an artist, an athlete, or a band.

(Before writing)

A. Write down the personal information you already know about the person or band. **Use** the internet to find the information you don't know: **nombre**, **edad**, **cumpleaños**, **país**, **ocupación**.

B. Read the texts from activity 6 in the Student Edition. You can use one of them as a model.

(Write the paragraph)

C. Write five sentences about the person or the band you have chosen.

Add a photo here if you'd like.

UNIDAD 1

Comunicación

LECCIÓN 1

PRESENTATIONAL

4 PRESENTATIONAL SPEAKING

You want to join the newspaper club for Spanish-speaking students as a reporter.
You need to leave a voice message with your personal information.

(Prepare the voice message)

A. Fill in this draft with your personal information.
This info can be made up.
Add a greeting and a closing.

> **SALUDO:** ....
>
> **MIS DATOS:**
>
> **Nombre:** Me llamo... ....
>
> **Edad:** ....
>
> **Cumpleaños:** ....
>
> **País / Ciudad de origen:** ....
>
> **Correo electrónico:** ....
>
> **Teléfono:** ....
>
> **DESPEDIDA:** ....

(Practice and record yourself)

B. Practice your message several times before recording it.
This will help you speak naturally and avoid making mistakes.

C. Record yourself leaving a voice message.
If you **don't read** your notes, your recording will sound much more natural.
Check your notes only if you don't remember what you need to say.

Comunicación

LECCIÓN 1

INTERPERSONAL

5 INTERPERSONAL WRITING

You are going to write a comment to answer a post from Dana's social media.

Read Dana's post

A. Search for a Hispanic American whose birthday is in the same month as yours. Throughout, several have been mentioned, but you can look for others on the internet.

Dana Hernández Seguir

Hay muchos hispanos famosos que viven en los Estados Unidos. Propongo un juego: ¿cumples años el mismo mes que una persona hispana famosa? ¡Preséntala aquí! #hispanosfamososUSA

1:14 PM - 26 ene 2021

1 Retweet **11** Me gusta

♡ 1   ⟳ 1   ♡ 11   ✉

B. Look for the following information about the person you have chosen so that you can describe them: **nombre**, **edad**, **país de origen**, **ocupación**.

Write the comment

C. Be sure to:

- use a greeting at the beginning.
- conjugate the verbs (**ser**, **tener**, **llamarse**) correctly.
- use **y** to connect sentences.

Responder a Dana Hernández   Responder

¡Hola! Yo cumplo años el mismo mes que...

....

....

....

....

....

After writing

D. Proofread before submitting your text.
Correct any mistakes you may find.

¿Qué idiomas hablas?

MI VOCABULARIO

UNIDAD 1

1 **RECUERDA: LOS DATOS PERSONALES • LOS IDIOMAS**

★★ **Listen to** four conversations about a photo album.
🔊 **Complete** these cards.

a Théo

NOMBRE: Se llama Théo.

EDAD: Tiene...

PAÍS: Es de...

IDIOMAS: Habla...

....

b Yelena

NOMBRE: ....

EDAD: ....

PAÍS: ....

IDIOMAS: ....

....

c Nigel

NOMBRE: ....

EDAD: ....

PAÍS: ....

IDIOMAS: ....

....

d Diane

NOMBRE: ....

EDAD: ....

PAÍS: ....

IDIOMAS: ....

....

¿Qué idiomas hablas?

MI VOCABULARIO

2 LOS IDIOMAS
★★ **Find** the nine languages hidden in the puzzle below.

L	I	N	G	L	É	S	S	O	S	T
Á	N	F	R	I	N	O	M	N	P	O
R	B	U	B	H	O	U	Z	I	O	I
A	L	E	M	Á	N	O	T	T	L	T
B	E	P	L	O	E	R	E	A	A	A
E	R	U	N	O	H	G	L	L	C	L
Ñ	U	Q	C	H	I	N	O	S	O	I
O	S	A	N	S	O	M	N	A	T	A
F	O	G	H	X	U	Q	U	R	A	N
A	Ñ	B	E	S	P	A	Ñ	O	L	O
P	O	R	T	U	G	U	É	S	O	C

ESTRATEGIAS

Learn what you need
You don't need to learn all the languages in the section **Mi vocabulario** of this unit. **Select the ones you need** to talk about yourself, the people around you, and the people and places you are interested in.

3 LOS IDIOMAS
★ What language(s) do these people speak?
Write complete sentences.

a. Yo hablo... ....

b. Mi papá ....

c. Mi mamá ....

d. Mi actor favorito o actriz favorita ....

4 LOS IDIOMAS
★ **Classify** the languages in the chart.

náhuatl   gallego

aymara   guaraní

catalán   quechua

vasco

LATINOAMÉRICA	ESPAÑA
náhuatl, ...	

UNIDAD 1

¿Qué idiomas hablas?

LECCIÓN 2

MI GRAMÁTICA

UNIDAD 1

5 REGULAR -AR VERBS • REGULAR -ER VERBS

★ **Put a mark** (✓) in the column under the correct subject pronouns for each sentence.

	YO	TÚ	ÉL / ELLA, USTED	NOSOTROS/AS	ELLOS / ELLAS, USTEDES
a. Aprendes español.		✓			
b. Habla inglés y español.					
c. Hablan cuatro idiomas.					
d. Aprendo francés.					
e. Hablamos italiano.					
f. Aprenden quechua.					

6 REGULAR -AR VERBS • REGULAR -ER VERBS

★★ **Complete** the sentences using the correct forms of the verbs in parentheses.

a. Daniel **(aprender)** ___aprende___ árabe en la escuela.

b. Mis papás y yo **(hablar)** _____ español en casa.

c. ¿**(Hablar, tú)** _____ quechua con tus papás?

d. Jenny y John **(practicar)** _____ español con sus amigos mexicanos.

e. Ustedes **(cantar)** _____ canciones muy bonitas *(very beautiful)* en italiano.

f. ¿Qué idiomas **(aprender, tú)** _____ en la escuela?

g. Nosotros **(cantar)** _____ canciones en español en la clase.

7 EXPRESSING CAUSE

★ **Underline** the correct answer.

a
¿Por qué / Porque hablas italiano?

b
Por qué / Porque mi mamá es italiana.

Es una cantante colombiana

LECCIÓN 2

MI VOCABULARIO

8 **LAS NACIONALIDADES**

★★ Dana is at **un campamento** (*a summer camp*).
Read her chat with her friend Guadalupe.
Complete the sentences below with the nationalities of Dana's summer camp friends.
Remember the adjectives must agree in number and gender with the people described.

DANA
¡Hola, Guada! 😃

GUADA
¡Dana! ¿Qué tal el campamento?

DANA
¡Genial!

GUADA
¿Son todos de los Estados Unidos como tú?

DANA
No, ¡somos de todo el mundo!
Hannah y Lena son de Alemania, Louise es de Francia, Paulo es de Portugal, Gustavo y Catalina son de Argentina, Zoë es de Canadá...

GUADA
¡Qué chido! 🌎

DANA
Luca es un muchacho de Italia... 😍 😍

GUADA
😱 😱 😱 ¿Tienes foto?

DANA
¡¡Noooo!! 😊
Hiromi es una muchacha de Japón, Lucía es del Perú y Octavio, de México.

GUADA
¡Es un campamento internacional!
¿En qué idioma hablan?

DANA
Hablamos en español, en inglés y en francés. 🥴

GUADA
¡Qué bien!

a. Dana es estadounidense.

b. Hannah y Lena son ....

c. Louise es ....

d. Paulo es ....

e. Gustavo y Catalina son ....

f. Zoë es ....

g. Luca es ....

h. Hiromi es ....

i. Lucía es ....

j. Octavio es ....

Es una cantante colombiana

MI VOCABULARIO

9 LAS NACIONALIDADES • RECUERDA: LAS OCUPACIONES

★ **Correct** the sentences to make them true.

a. Kilian Mbappé es un <u>artista japonés</u>.

Kilian Mbappé es un deportista francés.

b. Takashi Murakami es un <u>cantante colombiano</u>.

....

c. Lonzo y LaMelo Ball son unos <u>actores españoles</u>.

....

d. Penélope Cruz es una <u>astronauta costarricense</u>.

....

e. Franklin Chang-Díaz es un <u>deportista estadounidense</u>.

....

f. Juanes y Karol G son unos <u>deportistas franceses</u>.

....

Kilian Mbappé

Takashi Murakami

Lonzo y LaMelo Ball

Penélope Cruz

Franklin Chang- Díaz

Juanes y Karol G

10 RECUERDA: LOS DATOS PERSONALES

★ **Write** the appropriate questions to the following answers.

a. ● ¿Cómo te llamas .... ?

o Miriam García.

b. ● ¿ .... ?

o 42 años.

c. ● ¿ .... ?

o Soy fotógrafa.

d. ● ¿ .... ?

o De España.

e. ● ¿ .... ?

o Hablo español, gallego, inglés y portugués.

Es una cantante colombiana LECCIÓN 2

MI GRAMÁTICA

11 **GENDER AND NUMBER WITH ADJECTIVES OF NATIONALITY**
★★ **Fill in** the chart with the missing adjectives.

	SINGULAR		PLURAL	
	MASCULINE	FEMININE	MASCULINE	FEMININE
a. Australia	australiano	australiana		
b. Brasil			brasileños	
c. Canadá	canadiense			
d. Estados Unidos			estadounidenses	
e. Irlanda	irlandés			
f. España			españoles	
g. Israel	israelí			

12 **INDEFINITE ARTICLES**
★ **Complete** the sentences with the correct indefinite article.

a. Juan es ...un... amigo chileno de Mario.

b. Luc y Pierre son .... muchachos franceses.

c. Ana tiene .... profesor alemán.

d. Tienes .... profesores muy buenos.

e. Lima es .... ciudad peruana.

f. Querétaro es .... estado de México.

13 **INDEFINITE ARTICLES • GENDER AND NUMBER WITH ADJECTIVES OF NATIONALITY**
★★ **Write** the feminine form of each word in the following phrases.

a. un escritor alemán → ...una escritora alemana...

b. un estudiante japonés → ....

c. un fotógrafo español → ....

d. un deportista nicaragüense → ....

e. un juez boliviano → ....

UNIDAD 1

¿Dónde vives?

MI VOCABULARIO

UNIDAD 1

14 LOS LUGARES

★ Spanish students from different countries are posting photos.
Write where they live.

Marilisa Ferrara

¿En qué ciudad vivo?
#dondevivo

Nazir dos Santos

¿En qué país vivimos mis papás y yo? #dondevivo

James Kennard

¿En qué ciudad vivo?
#dondevivo

Anja Schultz

¿En qué ciudad vivimos Hannah y yo? #dondevivo

Sarah Smith

¿En qué país vivo?
#dondevivo

Elisabeth Martin

¿En qué país vivo?
#dondevivo

~~Pisa~~ Canadá Berlín Australia Nueva York Brasil

a. Marilisa Ferrara vive en Pisa.

b. Nazir dos Santos y sus papás viven en...

c. James Kennard

d. Anja y Hannah

e. Sarah Smith

f. Elisabeth Martin

¿Dónde vives?

● **MI VOCABULARIO**

15 LOS LUGARES

★ **Complete** the missing consonants to complete six words to talk about places.

| E | L | | P | A | Í | S |

| | A | | | I | U | | A |

| E | | | U | E | | O |

| | E | | E | | A | | O |

| | A | | | A | | I | | A |

| E | | | A | | I | | O |

16 LOS LUGARES

★ **Write** the names of different places in the Americas.
You can search on the internet.

a. La capital de Colombia → ....

b. Dos ciudades importantes de México → ....

c. Un país hispanoamericano que empiece *(begins)* por N → ....

d. Un barrio de Nueva York → ....

17 LOS LUGARES

★★ **Complete** the sentences with the correct word.

| ciudad | estado | capital | país | barrio |

a. Washington es la .... capital .... de los Estados Unidos.

b. Harlem es un .... de Manhattan.

c. Chicago es la .... más poblada del .... de Illinois.

d. México es un .... de Latinoamérica.

¿Dónde vives?

MI GRAMÁTICA

UNIDAD 1

18 REGULAR -IR VERBS • RECUERDA: REGULAR -AR AND -ER VERBS

★ **Write** the missing endings to complete the verb forms in present tense.

Pronombres	ESCUCHAR (listen)	LEER (read)	ESCRIBIR (write)
yo	escucho	le	escrib
tú	escuch	le	escrib
él / ella, usted	escuch	le	escrib
nosotros/as	escuch	le	escrib
vosotros/as	escuch	le	escrib
ellos / ellas, ustedes	escuch	le	escrib

19 REGULAR -IR VERBS • RECUERDA: REGULAR -AR AND -ER VERBS

★★ **Underline** the correct form of the verb.

a. • Y ustedes, ¿qué idiomas **hablan** / **hablen**?

   o Yo **hablas** / **hablo** dos y ella **habla** / **hablo** tres idiomas.

b. • Nosotros **estudiamos** / **estudiemos** chino.

c. • ¿Dónde **vivan** / **viven** ustedes?

   o **Vivamos** / **Vivimos** en los Estados Unidos.

d. • Y tú, ¿**leen** / **lees** revistas en español?

   o Sí, **leo** / **lees** la revista *Vida Latina*.

e. Blanca **escriba** / **escribe** correos electrónicos a sus amigos.

f. Santiago y yo **escuchamos** / **escuchemos** música en español.

20 REGULAR -IR VERBS • RECUERDA: REGULAR -AR AND -ER VERBS

★★★ **Write** four sentences about yourself and your friends, using these verbs.

a. (escuchar) → ....

b. (vivir) → ....

c. (leer) → ....

d. (escribir) → ....

Hispanos y latinos

MI VOCABULARIO

21 EL ORIGEN

★ **Put** the puzzle pieces **together** to form complete sentences.

a. Mi amigo se llama... ....

b. ....

c. ....

22 RECUERDA: LOS LUGARES • RECUERDA: LAS NACIONALIDADES

★★ **A. Unscramble** the syllables to form the names of five Central American countries.

1. má Pa na ⟶ Panamá ....

2. El dor va Sal ⟶ ....

3. Ri ta Cos ca ⟶ ....

4. te ma Gua la ⟶ ....

5. ca gua Ni ra ⟶ ....

B. Write the nationalities (masculine and feminine) that correspond to the countries above.

	MASCULINE	FEMININE
1	panameño	panameña
2		
3		
4		
5		

Hispanos y latinos

LECCIÓN 2

MI VOCABULARIO

23 **RECUERDA: DATOS SOBRE EL ESPAÑOL • RECUERDA: LOS NÚMEROS (1 Y 2)**

★★★ **A. Take** the cultural quiz.

You can review the ¡Empezamos! section in the Student Edition.

EL ESPAÑOL EN EL MUNDO

1. ¿De cuál de estos idiomas proviene el español?

○ **a.** Del ruso.

○ **b.** Del italiano.

○ **c.** Del latín.

2. ¿Quiénes llevan *(bring)* **el español a América?**

○ **a.** Los migrantes, en los siglos XIX (19) y XX (20).

○ **b.** Los colonizadores españoles, en los siglos XV (15) y XVI (16).

○ **c.** Los romanos, en el siglo II (dos).

3. ¿En cuántos países es el español el idioma oficial?

○ **a.** En tres países.

○ **b.** En veintiún países.

○ **c.** En cincuenta y cuatro países.

4. ¿En qué país de América del Sur no hablan español?

○ **a.** En Venezuela.

○ **b.** En Uruguay.

○ **c.** En Brasil.

5. Los brasileños...

○ **a.** son latinos y son hispanos.

○ **b.** son latinos, pero no son hispanos.

○ **c.** son hispanos, pero no son latinos.

6. Los españoles...

○ **a.** son latinos y son hispanos.

○ **b.** son latinos, pero no son hispanos.

○ **c.** son hispanos, pero no son latinos.

EL ESPAÑOL EN EL MUNDO

B. Listen to the answers and **give** yourself 10 points for each right answer. How many points did you get? **Spell out** your score.

.... puntos.

Hispanos y latinos

MI GRAMÁTICA

24 **RECUERDA: REGULAR AND IRREGULAR VERBS**

★ **Complete** the sentences using the correct form of the verbs in parentheses.

a. ¿Los amigos de Laura **(hablar)** ____hablan____ español?

b. Barbara y Lea **(ser)** _____ de origen alemán.

c. Juan **(aprender)** _____ italiano con sus amigos de Italia.

d. ¿Cómo **(llamarse)** _____ tu mamá?

   ¿De dónde **(ser)** _____?

e. ● Y ustedes, ¿dónde **(vivir)** _____?

   ○ Nosotros **(vivir)** _____ en Miami.

f. Marta **(tener)** _____ 24 años.

g. ¿Ustedes **(leer)** _____ libros en español?

ESTRATEGIA

Memorize regular and irregular forms

Memorizing the forms of **the most common regular and irregular verbs** will help you feel more confident when speaking and writing in Spanish.

25 **RECUERDA: DEFINITE AND INDEFINITE ARTICLES**

★★ **Underline** the correct answer.

a. Cusco es **la** / **una** ciudad del Perú.

b. Asunción es **la** / **una** capital de Paraguay.

c. Penélope Cruz y Javier Bardem son **los** / **unos** actores españoles.

d. **La** / **Una** protagonista de *Diario de una futura presidenta*

   se llama Elena Cañero-Reed.

e. ¿Cuándo es **el** / **un** cumpleaños de María?

f. **El** / **Un** español es el tercer *(third)* idioma en internet.

g. En mi barrio vive **el** / **un** muchacho español.

h. **Los** / **Unos** estados de Nevada y Florida tienen

   nombres de origen español.

i. Texas es **el** / **un** estado de los Estados Unidos.

j. *Diario de una futura presidenta* es **la** / **una** serie

   estadounidense.

Comunicación

UNIDAD 1

1 **INTERPRETIVE READING**

You are going to read a magazine article.

FAMOSOS MULTILINGÜES

El mundo del cine es multilingüe. Muchos actores y actrices de Hollywood hablan diferentes idiomas porque tienen orígenes diversos. Estrellas[1] hispanas populares como Penélope Cruz y Javier
5 Bardem hablan inglés y español, porque son españoles y trabajan[2] en los Estados Unidos.

Otras tienen habilidad para aprender idiomas: Jodie Foster habla francés y Gwyneth Paltrow habla español.

Natalie Portman

10 Algunos[3] profesionales del cine son totalmente bilingües por el origen de sus familias. La actriz y productora de cine Sandra Bullock habla muy bien alemán. ¿Por qué? Porque su mamá es una cantante de ópera alemana.

15 Y algunos tienen orígenes diversos y habilidad para aprender idiomas. Natalie Portman habla cinco idiomas: sus lenguas maternas[4] son el inglés y el hebreo, pero también habla español, alemán y japonés.

Viggo Mortensen

20 El actor estadounidense Viggo Mortensen habla inglés y danés, porque su papá es de Dinamarca. También habla perfectamente francés y español, porque vive en Barcelona. Y habla un poco de italiano, noruego, sueco y catalán.

1 stars   2 (they) work   3 some   4 mother tongues

UNIDAD 1

(Before reading)

A. Read the title of the article on the previous page and **look at** the pictures.
The words **famosos** and **multilingües** are cognates.
Guess what the title means. ....

(First reading)

B. Write how many languages these people speak.
Give the language(s) spoken.

1. Penélope Cruz y Javier Bardem hablan dos idiomas: inglés y español. ....

2. Jodie Foster ....

3. Gwyneth Paltrow ....

4. Sandra Bullock ....

5. Natalie Portman ....

6. Viggo Mortensen ....

(Second reading)

C. Read these sentences and **correct** them to make them true.
You may need to correct more than one word in each sentence.

1. La mamá de Sandra Bullock es una actriz italiana.

....

2. Natalie Portman aprende hebreo.

....

3. Viggo Mortensen habla perfectamente italiano, noruego, sueco y catalán.

....

(After reading)

D. Complete the sentence below.
You must **give** at least two reasons.

Muchos actores y actrices son multilingües porque tienen...

....

....

Comunicación

INTERPRETIVE

2 INTERPRETIVE LISTENING

You are going to listen to three interviews with people from Dana's neighborhood in Chicago.

Before listening

A. Read the names of the interviewees:
María Elena, **Paulo**, **Roberto**, **Heike**.
Guess where they are from. It's only a guess!
You could be wrong, but guessing before listening will help you better understand the interview.

First listen

B. Combine the words in the three columns to create a sentence relating on each interviewee.

1. María Elena	es de Alemania	y vive en los Estados Unidos.
2. Paulo	es de Brasil	y no habla español.
3. Roberto	es de los Estados Unidos	y su familia es de Venezuela.
4. Heike	es de los Estados Unidos	y su mamá es de Ecuador.

Second listen

C. Complete the sentences.

1. María Elena habla   español, ...

2. Paulo habla

3. Roberto habla

4. Heike habla

After listening

D. Write four sentences to introduce these people.

1. María Elena   es una muchacha...

2. Paulo

3. Roberto

4. Heike

Comunicación

PRESENTATIONAL

3 **PRESENTATIONAL WRITING**

Imagine that you have just created a blog to practice Spanish.
For your first blog post, write a paragragh introducing yourself.

(Write the presentation)

A. Follow the structure.

BIO

Write sentences about yourself: **nombre**, **edad**, **cumpleaños**, **nacionalidad**, **orígenes**, **dónde vives**, **idiomas**.

¡Hola! Me llamo...

....

....

....

....

....

....

....

Write one sentence to explain which languages are spoken by the people in your community.

....

....

....

....

....

(After writing)

B. Proofread before submitting your presentation.
Correct any mistakes you may find.

- Have you used the vocabulary from the unit? | Yes | No |
- Have you used the verbs **ser**, **tener**, **llamarse** and the regular verbs correctly? | Yes | No |
- Have your written compound sentences? | Yes | No |

Comunicación

PRESENTATIONAL

UNIDAD 1

4 **PRESENTATIONAL SPEAKING**

In a podcast, you are going to introduce someone from your social group that you consider to be interesting.

(Prepare the podcast)

A. Choose the person you want to interview.
Think of someone whose origins are diverse or who speaks more than one language to make your podcast more interesting.

B. Write a script in your notebook.

1. Take notes about the person you are interviewing:
nombre, **edad**, **cumpleaños**, **origen**, **idiomas**, **ocupación**, etc.

2. Use **y**, **pero**, **porque** and **también** to connect your ideas.

3. Be sure to **greet** your listeners and **use a closing** for your podcast.

¡Hola! Hoy presento a una persona de mi entorno. Se llama...

(Practice and record yourself)

C. Practice several times.
Pay attention to your pronunciation—it will count toward your grade!
Repeat the words or sentences that are especially difficult for you.

D. Record your podcast.
Make sure that you record in a quiet place that is free from interruptions.

Comunicación

LECCIÓN 2

INTERPERSONAL

5 **INTERPERSONAL WRITING**

You are going to comment about a social media post from a digital newspaper.

(Read the post)

A. Guess the meanings of the words you don't know by using context clues and cognates.

El Orden Mundial - EOM
@elOrdenMundial

(Seguir)

Un país multicultural: estos son los idiomas más hablados en cada estado de los EE. UU. después del inglés y el español.

Fuente: IPUMS USA

3:16 PM - 29 marzo 2017

(Write the comment)

B. You can write about something you found interesting in the infograph.
Here are some examples you may choose from:

- the diversity of languages in the United States
- information that is interesting or surprising to you
- the third language of your state and if you know someone that speaks it

Responder a El Orden Mundial - EOM   (Responder)

Para mí, es interesante el mapa porque...

NAME .... CLASS .... DATE ....

CULTURE QUIZ

1 **What percentage of the US population is of Hispanic or Latino origin?**

a. 5% ☐

b. 10% ☐

c. 20% ☐

2 **Which of these US states has a largest Hispanic population?**

a. Texas. ☐

b. New York. ☐

c. California. ☐

d. Florida. ☐

3 **Circle four countries from Central America.**

España Nicaragua Honduras

Ecuador Costa Rica Chile

Argentina Guatemala Perú

4 **What type of greeting is more appropiate when you are first introduced to someone, or in a formal setting?**

a. Un abrazo. ☐

b. Un apretón de manos. ☐

5 **El Día de Muertos is celebrated in...**

a. Mexico only. ☐

b. Mexico and Central America. ☐

c. all the Americas. ☐

6 **Circle four native languages spoken in Latin America.**

guaraní catalán vasco

náhuatl quechua

gallego aymara

7 **Where are catalán, gallego, and vasco spoken?**

a. Mexico. ☐

b. Spain. ☐

c. Argentina. ☐

8 **"Todas las personas que viven en Latinoamérica hablan español".**

a. True. ☐

b. False. ☐

9 **"Muchos peruanos son de origen chino o japonés".**

a. True. ☐

b. False. ☐

10 **"Muchos argentinos son de origen italiano o alemán".**

a. True. ☐

b. False. ☐

Reporteros 1

Amigos y familiares

1 **Watch** the video.
Answer the questions.

1. ¿Cuántos años tiene Sebastián?

2. ¿De dónde es?

3. ¿Qué idiomas habla?

4. ¿Cuáles son sus platos favoritos?

5. ¿Cuál es su deporte favorito?

6. ¿Qué cantantes de origen puertorriqueño menciona?

¿Te gusta bailar?

MI VOCABULARIO

2 LAS ACTIVIDADES

★★ **Look at** the objects in Sebastián's room.
Match the activities (**a–f**) with the correct objects (**1–6**) from the illustration.

a. comer chocolate ☐ 4

b. estudiar ☐

c. jugar al béisbol ☐

d. leer cómics ☐

e. escuchar música ☐

f. hacer deporte ☐

3 LAS ACTIVIDADES

★★★ **Match** the verb (**a–g**) with the corresponding words or phrases (**1–7**).

a. hacer

b. ver

c. salir

d. escuchar

e. jugar

f. leer

g. comer

1. al béisbol

2. series

3. con amigos o amigas

4. deporte

5. cómics

6. tostones

7. música

UNIDAD 2

¿Te gusta bailar?

MI VOCABULARIO

4 LAS ACTIVIDADES

★★ **Listen to** Sofía's interview.

🔊 Does she like to do these activities or not? **Put a mark** (✓) in the correct option.

5 LAS ACTIVIDADES

★★ **Match** the beginnings of the sentences (**a–d**) with the correct endings (**1–4**).

a. Tengo muchos cómics...

b. Me gusta escuchar música...

c. Me gusta comer chocolate...

d. No me gusta ver series...

1. ... y también tostones.

2. ... pero no me gusta bailar.

3. ... porque me gusta leer.

4. ... y tampoco ver la televisión.

6 LAS ACTIVIDADES

★★ What can you do to improve your Spanish?

a. Ver series...

b. Leer

c. Escuchar

d. Estudiar

UNIDAD 2

¿Te gusta bailar?

MI GRAMÁTICA

7 **GUSTAR** + INFINITIVE
★★ **Complete** the sentences with the correct form of **gustar**.

a. A mí .... bailar.

b. Y a ti, ¿................................... hacer deporte?

c. Y a usted, ¿................................... leer?

d. Y a ustedes, ¿qué .... hacer?

8 **GUSTAR** + INFINITIVE
★★ **Write** what these people like or don't like to do.

escuchar música	**a.** A mí no me gusta escuchar música.
comer chocolate	**b.** A mis amigos y a mí ....
leer cómics	**c.** A mi amiga Sara ....
estudiar	**d.** A mis amigos ....
jugar al béisbol	**e.** A nosotras ....

9 **AGREEMENT / DISAGREEMENT**
★★ **Complete** the sentences with **a mí también**, **a mí tampoco**, **a mí sí**, or **a mí no**.

a. ● A mí me gusta jugar al béisbol. ¿Y a ti?

○ .... ¡Me gusta hacer deporte!

b. ● A mí me gusta leer cómics.

○ .... Me gusta leer, pero no me gusta leer cómics.

c. ● A mí no me gusta bailar.

○ .... Me gusta escuchar música, pero no me gusta bailar.

– .... ¡Me gusta bailar y escuchar música!

¿Qué música te gusta?

MI VOCABULARIO

10 **LA MÚSICA • LOS INSTRUMENTOS • LOS ESTILOS**
★ **Underline** the correct word for each picture.

cantante / <u>banda</u> / compositor

música clásica / reguetón / jazz

guitarra / piano / batería

cantante / banda / instrumento

pop / salsa / rock

guitarra / piano / batería

11 **LA MÚSICA • LOS INSTRUMENTOS • LOS ESTILOS**
★★ **Find** the odd one out in each series.

a. la batería   la guitarra   la canción   el piano

b. la salsa   el reguetón   el rock   la banda

c. cantar   tocar   escuchar   jugar

d. el / la cantante   el / la compositor/a   el / la artista   el instrumento

UNIDAD 2

¿Qué música te gusta? ████████████████████ LECCIÓN 1

MI VOCABULARIO

12 LA MÚSICA • LOS INSTRUMENTOS • LOS ESTILOS
★★ **Complete** the paragraphs with the correct words.

compositor | banda | cantante | canción | batería | piano | rock | estilos

---

Mis amigos y yo tenemos una **ª**<u>banda</u> musical. Nos llamamos Los Boricuas.

Yo toco el **b** ...., Mariela toca la **c** ....

Alejandra es la **d** .... de la banda y Omar es el **e** ....

Tenemos una **f** .... de momento:
"¿Qué es lo que hay?". Nos gusta mucho porque es
un saludo típico de Puerto Rico.

A los cuatro nos gustan muchos **g** ....
musicales, pero nuestros favoritos son el reguetón
y el **h** ....

---

13 LA MÚSICA • LOS INSTRUMENTOS • LOS ESTILOS
★★★ **Decide** whether the following sentences are true (**T**) or false (**F**).
Correct the false sentences.

a. Una banda es un grupo de músicos. ☒ F

....

b. El jazz, el pop y el rock son estilos de música. T F

....

c. El piano, la guitarra y la batería son estilos de música. T F

....

d. Un compositor o una compositora escribe las canciones. T F

....

e. Daddy Yankee es un cantante de música clásica. T F

....

¿Qué música te gusta?

MI GRAMÁTICA

14 **GUSTAR** + NOUN

★ **Underline** the correct answer for each sentence.

a. A mi hermana le gustan **el rock** / **las bandas de rock**.

b. ● ¿Te gusta **la música** / **las canciones de reguetón**?

   ○ Sí, pero no me gustan **la música clásica** / **los estilos urbanos**.

c. Me gustan mucho **el pop** / **las canciones pop**.

d. Me gusta mucho **la compositora** / **los cantantes** de la banda Buscabullas.

e. A mi mamá le gustan mucho **la guitarra** / **las guitarras**.

15 **GUSTAR** + NOUN ● **RECUERDA:** **GUSTAR** + INFINITIVE

★★ **Complete** the sentences with the correct form of **gustar**.

a. A mí ..me gustan.. las canciones de reguetón.

b. ¿A ti .... diferentes estilos de música?

c. A mi mejor amiga .... tocar la guitarra,

   pero no .... cantar.

d. A mis amigos y a mí no .... la música clásica.

e. A Yolanda y a Andrés .... un cantante de salsa puertorriqueño

   que se llama Héctor Lavoe.

f. ¿A ustedes .... los artistas de reguetón?

g. A mis papás no .... escuchar música pop.

16 **GUSTAR** + NOUN AND INFINITIVE VERBS ● QUANTIFIERS (1): **MUCHO**

★★ **Write** about your musical preferences using complete sentences.

🖤🖤 **a.** Me gusta/n mucho → ....

🖤 **b.** Me gusta/n → ....

c. No me gusta/n → ....

Mi animal favorito

MI VOCABULARIO

UNIDAD 2

17 **LOS ANIMALES Y LAS MASCOTAS**

★★ **Unscramble** the syllables to form the word for each animal.

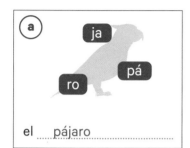

a ja / pá / ro

el ___pájaro___

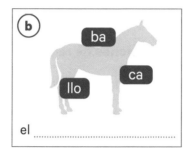

b ba / ca / llo

el _____

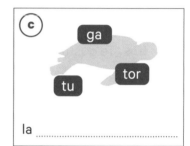

c ga / tor / tu

la _____

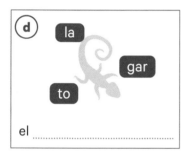

d la / gar / to

el _____

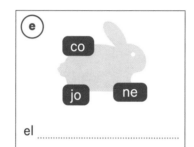

e co / jo / ne

el _____

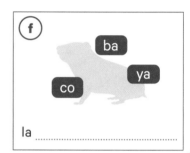

f ba / ya / co

la _____

18 **LA PERSONALIDAD (1) • LAS CARACTERÍSTICAS**

★★★ **Describe** the animals from activity 17 with an adjective.

a. ___Los pájaros son ágiles.___

b. _____

c. _____

d. _____

e. _____

f. _____

19 **LA PERSONALIDAD (1) • LAS CARACTERÍSTICAS**

★★ Sebastián and Guada's pets are total opposites.
Describe Guada's pet with the opposite adjectives.
Pay attention to the noun-adjective agreement.

El perro de Sebastián es...	La tortuga de Guada es...	
grande		pequeña
nervioso		
rápido		
cariñoso		
divertido		
feo		

Mi animal favorito

● **MI VOCABULARIO**

20 **LA PERSONALIDAD (1) • LOS ANIMALES Y LAS MASCOTAS**
★★ **A. Take** this personality test.

🔊 ¿Qué animal eres?

1. Tu libro favorito es...
○ **a.** una historia (*story*) real, por ejemplo, una biografía.
○ **b.** un libro de aventuras o de ciencia ficción.
○ **c.** una historia de amor (*love*).

2. Entre estos tres, tu personaje favorito es...
○ **a.** el león Mufasa, de *El rey León*, porque es el líder.
○ **b.** la pantera Bagheera, de *El libro de la selva*, porque es independiente.
○ **c.** la gorila Kala, de *Tarzán*, porque es leal.

3. Tus vacaciones ideales son...
○ **a.** ¡Todas las vacaciones son ideales!
○ **b.** con amigos y amigas.
○ **c.** en familia.

4. La foto que tienes en la pantalla de tu celular
(*your cell phone's screen*) **es...**
○ **a.** una foto de tu cantante o deportista favorito / favorita.
○ **b.** una foto relacionada con tus amigos y amigas.
○ **c.** una foto relacionada con tu familia.

B. Check your answers and **read** your profile. Do you agree? [Yes] [No]

MAYORÍA DE RESPUESTAS (a)	MAYORÍA DE RESPUESTAS (b)	MAYORÍA DE RESPUESTAS (c)
Eres inteligente y también abierto / abierta y te gusta liderar. Sabes lo que quieres (*You know what you want*).	Eres independiente y divertido / divertida. Tu actividad favorita es salir con amigos y amigas.	Eres simpático / simpática y cariñoso / cariñosa. Te gusta estar con tu familia y con la gente que quieres (*you love*).
Eres un .	**Eres un** .	**Eres un** .

Mi animal favorito
LECCIÓN 1

MI GRAMÁTICA

21 **NOUN-ADJECTIVE AGREEMENT**

★ **Put a mark** (✓) in the columns that apply.

	SINGULAR	PLURAL	MASCULINE	FEMININE
a. el gato	✓		✓	
b. la tortuga				
c. los perros				
d. el pez				
e. las cobayas				
f. el manatí				

22 **NOUN-ADJECTIVE AGREEMENT**

★★ **Fill in** the blanks with the correct endings for the adjectives.

a. Me gustan mucho los perros porque son inteligent_es___ y divertid_os___.

b. La mascota de Marta es muy cariños_____. ¡Tiene un gato súper bonit_____!

c. El manatí es un animal representativ_____ de Puerto Rico.

d. No me gustan los lagartos. Para mí, son fe_____ y aburrid_____.

e. El coquí es una rana pequeñ_____ que solo existe en Puerto Rico.

f. Las cobayas son muy nervios_____ y muy divertid_____.

23 **QUANTIFIERS (1 Y 2):** MUY , MUCHO , UN POCO

★★ **Underline** the correct quantifier.

a. Mi perro es **muy** / **un poco** inteligente. Se llama Rex y es un labrador.

b. Me gustan **muy** / **mucho** las tortugas. ¡En mi familia tenemos dos!

   Son tranquilas y **muy** / **un poco** bonitas. También son **mucho** / **un poco** lentas.

c. Me gusta **muy** / **mucho** hacer deporte. ¡Mi deporte favorito es el béisbol!

d. Los elefantes son unos animales **muy** / **mucho** grandes.

e. Me gusta **muy** / **mucho** la música latina: la salsa, el reguetón, etc.

f. Mi lagarto es **muy** / **mucho** tranquilo, pero es **mucho** / **un poco** distante.

¿Cómo es La Borinqueña?

● **MI VOCABULARIO**

24 **LA PERSONALIDAD (1 Y 2)**

★ Miles Morales is the new Spider-Man. **Read** the text about him.
Describe Miles Morales and Ganke Lee's personalities.

🔊 Miles Morales es un muchacho de Brooklyn (Nueva York). Tiene trece años y es el nuevo Hombre Araña *(Spider-Man)*.

Miles es un muchacho inteligente y trabajador. Habla inglés y también español porque su mamá es de Puerto Rico. Su papá es afroamericano. Es abierto y es muy creativo. Le gusta hacer grafitis y salir con sus amigos. Cuando Miles es *Spider-Man*, es muy ágil y rápido. También es muy valiente.

El mejor amigo de Miles es Ganke Lee. Es amable, simpático y leal.

a. Miles Morales es ....

b. Ganke Lee es ....

25 **LA PERSONALIDAD (2)**

★ **Choose** the correct adjective for each sentence.

| creativa | abierta | tímida | trabajadora | perezosa | valiente |

a. No te gusta trabajar. Eres una persona _perezosa._

b. Tienes mucha imaginación. Eres una persona ....

c. No eres tímido / tímida. Eres una persona ....

d. No eres sociable. Eres una persona ....

e. Te gusta mucho trabajar. Eres una persona ....

f. No eres cobarde *(coward)*. Eres una persona ....

26 **LA PERSONALIDAD (1 Y 2)**

★★ What is a good friend like? **Complete** the sentence.

Para mí, un buen amigo o una buena amiga es una persona...

....

UNIDAD 2

¿Cómo es La Borinqueña?

MI VOCABULARIO

27 LA PERSONALIDAD (1 Y 2)

★★ **Listen to** a podcast about these celebrities from Puerto Rico.

🔊 **Describe** their personalities using the adjectives below.

trabajador / trabajadora	creativo / creativa	inteligente	amable
simpático / simpática	cariñoso / cariñosa	independiente	valiente
divertido / divertida	abierto / abierta	tímido / tímida	

a. Daddy Yankee es... ....

b. Jennifer Lopez es... ....

c. Raquel Sofía es... ....

d. Bad Bunny es... ....

28 LA PERSONALIDAD (1 Y 2)

★★ What are these people like? **Write** complete sentences.

a. Yo → Yo soy... ....

....

b. Mi amigo / amiga → ....

....

c. Mi profesor / profesora → ....

....

d. Mi papá / mamá → ....

....

UNIDAD 2

¿Cómo es La Borinqueña?

MI GRAMÁTICA

29 RECUERDA: GUSTAR + NOUN AND INFINITIVE VERBS

★★ **Write** sentences about yourself that are true, using the words below.
Use gustar in the correct form.

EL CHOCOLATE

BAILAR

LOS PERROS

TOCAR LA GUITARRA

EL BÉISBOL

LEER CÓMICS

LA MÚSICA CLÁSICA

a. A mis amigos y a mí ....

b. A mis papás ....

c. A mi profesor / profesora ....

d. A mis amigos ....

30 RECUERDA: NOUN-ADJECTIVE AGREEMENT

★★ **Put a mark** (✓) in the column under the correct gender.
Write the missing masculine or feminine form.

	MASCULINE	FEMININE
a. un gato pequeño	✓	una gata pequeña
b. la muchacha inteligente		
c. el compositor creativo		
d. una deportista rápida		
e. un cantante tímido		

Comunicación

INTERPRETIVE

1 INTERPRETIVE READING

You are going to read a text about two friends.

PETER Y TOMÁS

¡Hola! Me llamo Peter y tengo una familia que me adora. Me gusta mucho jugar con mis amigos en el parque y hacer deporte. ¡Soy muy ágil y rápido! También me gusta comer chocolate especial para perros. Es mi comida favorita.

Tomás es mi mejor amigo. Es muy, muy cariñoso y divertido. Me gusta salir
5 con él, pero no me gusta ver la televisión con él. A él le gusta mucho ver series, pero a mí no. Hay otra cosa que no me gusta: los gatos. Son un poco distantes y creo que no son leales. Yo soy leal y también muy cariñoso.

UNIDAD 2

Copyright © by Difusión, S. L.

UNIDAD 2

(Before reading)

A. Look at the picture and **read** the title of the article on the previous page.
Who are Peter and Tomás?

1. Dos muchachos. ☐

2. Dos mascotas. ☐

3. Un muchacho y su mascota. ☐

4. Un muchacho y su papá. ☐

(Read the article)

B. Who is Peter and who is Tomás?
Label the picture.

(Read the article again)

C. Answer the questions in complete sentences.

1. ¿Cómo es Peter? *Write four adjectives.* ....

....

2. ¿Qué le gusta hacer a Peter? ....

....

3. ¿Qué animales no le gustan a Peter? ¿Por qué? ....

....

Comunicación

INTERPRETIVE

2 INTERPRETIVE LISTENING

You are going to listen to Guillermo's podcast about his friends.

🔊 (First listen)

A. Who likes or doesn't like these things?

Fill in the chart with the correct person (**Mariana**, **Joel**, **Nilson**, or **Guillermo**).

	LE GUSTA(N) ♥	NO LE GUSTA(N) 👎
escuchar música	Mariana, ...	
bailar		
ver series		
leer		
estudiar		
los animales		
hacer deporte		
salir con amigos y amigas		

🔊 (Second listen)

B. Answer the questions in complete sentences.

1. ¿Cuál es el estilo de música favorito de Mariana? ....

2. ¿En qué gustos coinciden Joel y Guillermo? ....

....

3. ¿Qué deporte le gusta mucho a Joel? ....

4. ¿Cuál es la actividad favorita de Nilson? ....

5. ¿Qué animales tiene Guillermo? ....

UNIDAD 2

Comunicación

PRESENTATIONAL

3 **PRESENTATIONAL WRITING**

You are going to write a blog post to introduce your best friend.

(Before writing)

A. Read the text about La Borinqueña in the Student Edition.
It will help you write your article.

(Write the article)

B. Follow the structure.

UNIDAD 2

Answer the questions
in complete sentences:

- ¿Cómo se llama?
- ¿Cuántos años tiene?
- ¿Cómo es su
  personalidad?
- ¿Qué le gusta
  y qué no le gusta?

(After writing)

C. Proofread before submitting your writing.
Correct any mistakes you may find.

- Have you used the verb **gustar** correctly? | Yes | | No |
- Have you used the quantifiers **mucho**, **muy**, and **un poco** correctly? | Yes | | No |
- Have you checked the noun-adjective agreement? | Yes | | No |

Comunicación

PRESENTATIONAL

4 **PRESENTATIONAL SPEAKING**
Imagine that you are a vlogger.
You are going to record a video about what you like and don't like to do.

(Prepare the video)
A. Write the script in your notebook.

1. Include two activities that you like and two activities that you don't like.

> Me gusta (mucho)...
> No me gusta...

2. Say what animals you like.
Describe their personality traits.

> Me gustan los perros porque son...

3. Explain what kind of music you like.
Say who is your favorite singer or band.

> Mi estilo de música favorito es...

4. Add a greeting and a closing to your script.

(Practice and record yourself)
B. Practice several times.
Pay attention to your pronunciation—it will count toward your grade!
Repeat the words or sentences that are especially difficult for you.

C. Record your video.
Make sure that you record in a quiet place
that is free from interruptions.

UNIDAD 2

Comunicación

INTERPERSONAL

5 INTERPERSONAL WRITING

You are going to reply to Sebastián's latest social media post.

Read Sebastián's post

A. Underline all the questions you can find in the post.

Sebastián

Me gustan mucho los animales, especialmente los perros, ¡son muy cariñosos! También me gusta mucho la música, sobre todo dos estilos musicales: el reguetón y la salsa. Me gustan mucho las canciones de Marc Anthony y de Daddy Yankee: ¡son mis cantantes favoritos! ¡Ah! Y también me gusta mucho bailar. Y a ustedes, ¿qué les gusta? ¿Cuáles son sus gustos musicales? ¿Y cuál es su animal favorito?

#megustanlosanimales #reguetón

Write the comment

B. Answer all his questions.
Say if you agree with him or not. **Use a mí también** or **a mí no** accordingly.

Responder a Sebastián	Responder

....

....

....

....

....

....

....

UNIDAD 2

Mi círculo

MI VOCABULARIO

1 **LA FAMILIA (1 Y 2)**

★★ **Look at** Sebastián's family tree.
Complete the sentences below with the correct family vocabulary.

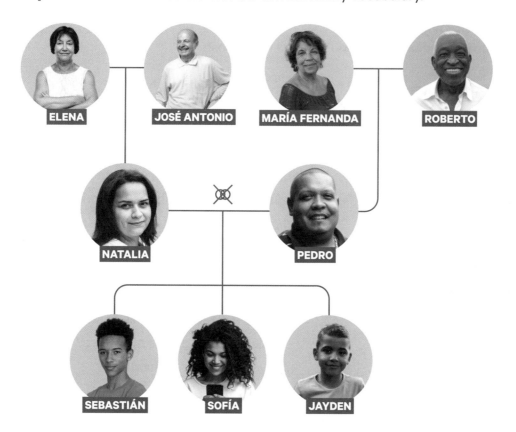

a. José Antonio es...

1. el ....._papá_..... de Natalia.

2. el .... de Sebastián.

3. el .... de Elena.

b. Jayden es...

1. el .... de Sofía.

2. el .... de Natalia y Pedro.

3. el .... de María
   Fernanda y Roberto.

c. María Fernanda es...

1. la .... de Sebastián.

2. la .... de Pedro.

3. la .... de Roberto.

d. Natalia es...

1. la .... de Sebastián.

2. la .... de Pedro.

3. la .... de Elena
   y José Antonio.

UNIDAD 2

Mi círculo

MI VOCABULARIO

2 **LA FAMILIA (1 Y 2)**

★★ **Complete** each sentence with the correct family vocabulary.

a. La mamá de mi mamá es mi ____abuela____.

b. Mi hermana es la _____ de mi abuelo.

c. La hija de mi mamá y de mi papá es mi _____.

d. Mi mamá es la _____ de mis abuelos.

e. El hijo de mi abuelo es mi _____.

f. Mi papá es el _____ de mi mamá. Están **separados** *(They are separated)*.

3 **LA FAMILIA (1 Y 2)**

★★ **Read** the sentences below.
Write the name of each member of the family tree.

a. Andrés es el papá de Carla.

b. Andrés es el hijo de Lola.

c. Lola es la esposa de Antonio.

d. Ana es la exesposa de Andrés.

e. Juan es el esposo de Ana.

f. Nacho es el hermano de Carla.

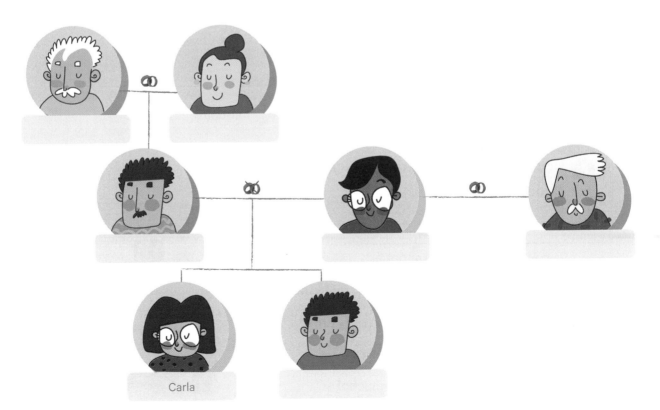

Carla

UNIDAD 2

Copyright © by Difusión, S. L.

Mi círculo

MI GRAMÁTICA

4 **POSSESSION WITH** DE

★ **Look at** Sebastián's family tree in the Student Edition.
Answer the questions by **describing** how Sebastián and these people are related to each other.
Write complete sentences, using a **de** phrase to show possession.

a. ¿Quién es Sofía? Sofía es la hermana de Sebastián.

b. ¿Quién es Natalia? ....

c. ¿Quién es Jayden? ....

d. ¿Quién es Pedro? ....

e. ¿Quiénes son Elena, José Antonio, María Fernanda y Roberto? ....

....

5 **POSSESSIVE ADJECTIVES (1)**

★★ **Read** the sentences and **look at** the underlined words.
Fill in the blanks with the correct possessive.

a. Yo vivo en San José. → San José es ...mi... ciudad.

b. Yo tengo dos hermanas: Sofía y Valentina. → Sofía y Valentina son .... hermanas.

c. Tú tienes unas amigas que se llaman Carla y Sara. → Carla y Sara son .... amigas.

d. Yo tengo un perro que se llama Rony. → Rony es .... perro.

e. Yo soy hijo de Sonia y de Pedro. → Sonia y Pedro son .... papás.

f. Tú tienes un abuelo muy divertido. → Es .... abuelo.

6 **POSSESSIVE ADJECTIVES (1) • ACCENT MARKS**

★★ **Underline** the correct option.

a. • ¿Cómo se llama **tu** / **tú** hermano?

   o Pablo, como **mi** / **mí** papá.

b. • El muchacho de la foto es **mi** / **mí** hermano Júnior.

   o Y el otro muchacho, ¿quién es? ¿Eres **tu** / **tú**?

c. • No me gusta la música clásica.

   o ¡Pues a **mi** / **mí** me gusta mucho!

Familias con talento

LECCIÓN 2

MI VOCABULARIO

7 **LA FAMILIA (1, 2, 3 Y 4)**

★★ **Look at** the family tree of the characters from *Modern Family.*
Complete the sentences below with the correct family words.

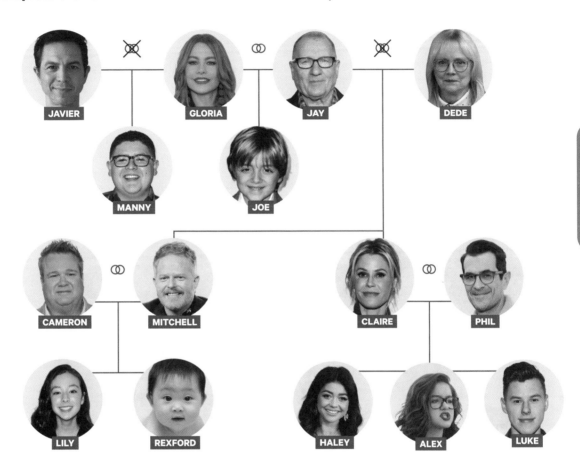

a. Javier es el ....papá.... de Manny.

b. Jay es el .... de Manny.

c. Claire es la .... de Lily y Rexford.

d. Haley, Alex y Luke son los .... de Cameron y Mitchell.

e. Gloria y Jay son los .... de Joe.

f. Lily y Rexford son los .... de Haley, Alex y Luke.

g. Luke es el .... de Lily.

h. Javier es el .... de Gloria, y Dede es la .... de Jay.

i. Joe es el .... de Manny.

UNIDAD 2

Familias con talento

MI VOCABULARIO

8 **LA FAMILIA (4)**

★ **Fill in** the blanks with the missing family vocabulary.

a. el tío + la tía = _los tíos_

b. la tía + la tía = ...

c. el tío + el tío = ...

d. el primo + el primo = ...

e. .... + la prima = las primas

f. el primo + la prima = ...

9 **LA FAMILIA (1, 2, 3 Y 4)**

★★★ **Look at** the pictures of these four families.

🔊 **Listen to** four people talking about their families.

Match each person (**1–4**) with the corresponding picture (**a–d**).

UNIDAD 2

Familias con talento ▭▭▭▭▭▭▭▭▭▭▭▭ LECCIÓN 2

MI GRAMÁTICA

⑩ POSSESSIVE ADJECTIVES (2)
★★ **Look at** Sebastián's family tree in the Student Edition.
Answer the questions below in complete sentences.

a. ¿Roberto es el papá de Sebastián? _No, Roberto es su abuelo._

b. ¿Pedro es el padrastro de Sebastián? ....

c. ¿Natalia es la tía de Sebastián? ....

d. ¿Elena es la nieta de Sebastián? ....

e. ¿Sofía y Jayden son los primos de Sebastián? ....

⑪ POSSESSIVE ADJECTIVES (2)
★★ **Read** the sentences and **look at** the underlined words.
Fill in the blanks with the correct possessive adjective.

a. Sebastián tiene un hermanastro: Jayden.

→ Jayden es ___su___ hermanastro.

b. Inés y Lucas son amigos de Carla y de Sara.

→ Carla y Sara son .... amigas.

c. Cameron es el tío de Alex.

→ Cameron es .... tío.

d. Mi familia y yo tenemos un perro que se llama Haiku.

→ Haiku es .... perro.

e. Andrea, Sandra y Sebastián van al mismo (the same) colegio.

→ Es .... colegio.

f. La madrastra de Sonia se llama Gloria.

→ Gloria es .... madrastra.

g. Mi hermano y yo tenemos tres primas.

→ Son .... primas.

h. Susana tiene dos gatos muy bonitos y cariñosos.

→ Son .... gatos.

ESTRATEGIAS

Make your own charts
To better understand and memorize possessive adjectives, **you can create a chart and highlight in different colors the forms** you may find difficult. You can also translate them into English.

UNIDAD 2

Copyright © by Difusión, S. L.

Arte en Puerto Rico

MI VOCABULARIO

12 **LAS PARTES DEL CUERPO**

★ **Match** the words with the body parts.

el pelo | a

la boca |

la cabeza |

los ojos |

la nariz |

las manos |

las orejas |

13 **LA DESCRIPCIÓN FÍSICA (1)**

★★ **Read** the descriptions and **look at** the illustrations.
Match each description (**a–f**) with the corresponding person (**1–15**).

a. Tiene el pelo rubio, corto y rizado. 11

b. Tiene el pelo negro, rizado y muy largo.

c. No tiene pelo. Lleva barba. Tiene la nariz grande.

d. Tiene el pelo rubio, largo y liso. Lleva lentes.

e. Tiene el pelo corto y negro. Lleva bigote, pero no lleva barba.

f. Tiene el pelo corto, rizado y castaño. No lleva lentes.

Arte en Puerto Rico

MI VOCABULARIO

14 **LA DESCRIPCIÓN FÍSICA (1)**

★ **Look at** the pictures of three Puerto Rican personalities.
Write their physical descriptions in complete sentences.
Note that you need to **make** the noun-adjective agreement.

Mayra Santos-Febres
escritora y profesora

Mayra Santos-Febres tiene el pelo...

Alexis Díaz
muralista

c

Adamari López
actriz y presentadora
de televisión

UNIDAD 2

Arte en Puerto Rico

LECCIÓN 2

MI GRAMÁTICA

15 **RECUERDA: NOUN-ADJECTIVE AGREEMENT**

★ **Read** the information about two Puerto Rican artists.
Each text contains four agreement mistakes: **find** and **correct** them.

Ricky Martin es un cantante y actor puertorriqueño.
                                    corto
Tiene el pelo ~~cortos~~ y lisos. Tiene los ojos marrones.

Lleva barba y bigote. Es muy divertida y muy valientes.

Sofía Maldonado-Suárez es pintora y muralista.

Tiene el pelo larga y lisa. Tiene los ojos verde.

Es una mujer inteligente, simpático y divertida.

16 **RECUERDA: NOUN-ADJECTIVE AGREEMENT**

★★ **A. Put a mark** (✓) in the correct adjective to describe each noun below.

1. la cabeza
- pequeño ☐
- pequeña ✓
- pequeños ☐
- pequeñas ☐

2. el pelo
- rizado ☐
- rizada ☐
- rizados ☐
- rizadas ☐

3. la boca
- grande ☐
- grandes ☐

4. las orejas
- pequeño ☐
- pequeña ☐
- pequeños ☐
- pequeñas ☐

5. el pelo
- corto ☐
- corta ☐
- cortos ☐
- cortas ☐

6. los ojos
- marrón ☐
- marrones ☐

B. Look at Sebastián's picture.
Write a short paragraph describing his physical appearance.

Sebastián tiene el pelo...
....
....
....

¿Quién es quién?

MI VOCABULARIO

17 LA DESCRIPCIÓN FÍSICA (1 Y 2)

★★ A film director is looking for an actor and an actress for his / her new movie.
Read the casting description and **look at** the illustrations.
Put a mark (✓) in the boxes of the two people who best fit the casting description.

Eric
1.73 m
(5 ft. 8 in.)

Sam
1.82 m
(5 ft. 11 in.)

David
1.77 m
(5 ft. 10 in.)

Leo
1.71 m
(5 ft. 7 in.)

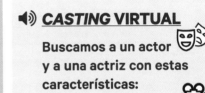

🔊 **CASTING VIRTUAL**

Buscamos a un actor
y a una actriz con estas
características:

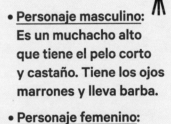

• Personaje masculino:
Es un muchacho alto
que tiene el pelo corto
y castaño. Tiene los ojos
marrones y lleva barba.

• Personaje femenino:
Es una muchacha baja
que tiene el pelo liso y
largo. No lleva lentes.
Tiene los ojos marrones.

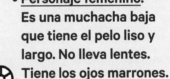

Mike
1.69 m
(5 ft. 6 in.)

Joe
1.75 m
(5 ft. 9 in.)

Jesús
1.62 m
(5 ft. 7 in.)

Ben
1.70 m
(5 ft. 7 in.)

Jordan
1.95 m
(6 ft. 5 in.)

Al
1.65 m
(5 ft. 5 in.)

Laura
1.62 m
(5 ft. 4 in.)

Kate
1.70 m
(5 ft. 7 in.)

Kim
1.68 m
(5 ft. 6 in.)

Emma
1.62 m
(5 ft. 4 in.)

Mia
1.52 m
(4 ft. 11 in.)

Carmen
1.56 m
(5 ft. 1 in.)

Rachel
1.64 m
(5 ft. 5 in.)

Sofia
1.62 m
(5 ft. 4 in.)

Olivia
1.69 m
(5 ft. 6 in.)

Ann
1.64 m
(5 ft. 5 in.)

UNIDAD 2

¿Quién es quién?

MI VOCABULARIO

18 **LA DESCRIPCIÓN FÍSICA (1 Y 2) • RECUERDA: LA FAMILIA (1)**
★★ **Look at** these two pictures of Francisco's family and **find** all eight differences.
Write complete sentences describing the differences.
Use family vocabulary.

1. En la imagen A, la hermana de Francisco es baja. En la imagen B, es...

2. ....

....

3. ....

....

4. ....

....

....

5. ....

....

....

6. ....

....

7. ....

....

....

8. ....

....

Francisco

Francisco

UNIDAD 2

¿Quién es quién?

MI GRAMÁTICA

19 **RECUERDA: POSSESSION WITH DE** • **RECUERDA: POSSESSIVE ADJECTIVES**

★★ **A. Match** each caption (**1-6**) with the corresponding illustration (**a-f**).

1. Mi amigo Nacho con su perro. [d]

2. La profesora de mi hermana pequeña con su hija, María. [ ]

3. Mi primo Alberto con su mujer. [ ]

4. Mi mejor amiga con sus hermanas y hermanos. [ ]

5. Los abuelos de mi hermanastro. [ ]

6. Mis tíos con sus hijos, Eva y Dave. [ ]

B. Translate the captions above into English.

1. ....

2. ....

3. ....

4. ....

5. ....

6. ....

20 **RECUERDA: NOUN-ADJECTIVE AGREEMENT**

★★ **Combine** the words in the three columns to make meaningful sentences.

a. Mi papá y yo	tienen	muy cariñosos.
b. Mi madrastra	son	los ojos azules.
c. Mis hermanas	llevamos	alta.
d. Mi tío y mi tía	es	lentes.

UNIDAD 2

Comunicación

INTERPRETIVE

1 INTERPRETIVE READING

You are going to read an email from Johanna to Ignacio, an exchange student.

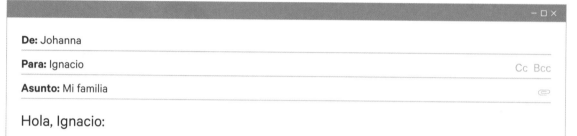

— □ ×

De: Johanna

Para: Ignacio   Cc Bcc

Asunto: Mi familia

Hola, Ignacio:

¿Qué tal? Hoy te hablo de mi familia.

Mi papá se llama John. Tiene 41 años, es muy alto y lleva barba.

No tengo hermanos, pero tengo dos primos muy simpáticos: Louis y Diane.
Louis tiene 8 años y es el hijo de mi tía Sofía. Sofía es muy cariñosa. Es un poco baja y tiene el pelo castaño, largo y liso.

Mi otra prima, Diane, tiene 6 años y es la hija de mi tío Lorenzo. Diane es la pequeña de la familia. Tiene el pelo largo y rizado. Su mamá se llama Martha y tiene el pelo muy corto y rizado.

Por último, están mis abuelos: Michael y Margaret. Mi abuelo es un poco tímido, pero es muy amable. Mi abuela es una mujer muy inteligente y divertida.
En la foto tiene el pelo corto y liso.

Te envío una foto. ¿Quién es quién?

Hasta muy pronto,

Johanna

← Responder   → Reenviar

UNIDAD 2

(First reading)

A. Decide whether the sentences below are true (**T**) or false (**F**).
Correct the false sentences.

1. El papá de Johanna se llama John.   T   F

....

2. Johanna tiene dos hermanos pequeños.   T   F

....

3. Louis y Diane son los tíos de Johanna.   T   F

....

4. Las tías de Johanna se llaman Sofía y Martha.   T   F

....

5. Los abuelos de Johanna son muy divertidos.   T   F

....

(Second reading)

B. Write the name of each family member.
Say how Johanna is related to each of them.

a ....   f ....

b ....   g ....

c ....   h ....

Johanna ....   i ....

d ....   e ....

Comunicación

INTERPRETIVE

2 INTERPRETIVE LISTENING

You are going to listen to a podcast about different types of Puerto Rican families.

(Before listening)

A. Look at the illustrations.

Match each illustration (**a–e**) with a description below (**1–5**).

1. Un abuelo, una abuela y una nieta ☐

2. Dos esposos sin hijos ☐

3. Un papá, una mamá y un hijo ☐

4. Una mamá y un hijo ☐

5. Un papá, un hijo y una hija ☐

(First listen)

B. Put the illustrations **in order** according to when they are described in the podcast.

(Second listen)

C. Decide whether the sentences are true (**T**) or false (**F**).

1. En Puerto Rico, la familia es muy importante. ☐T ☐F

2. Las familias boricuas tienen 3 miembros aproximadamente. ☐T ☐F

3. El 67.10 % de las familias de Puerto Rico no tienen hijos. ☐T ☐F

4. Las familias monoparentales *(single-parent)* más frecuentes no tienen papá. ☐T ☐F

5. En Puerto Rico, la mayoría de los abuelos y abuelas viven con sus nietos. ☐T ☐F

UNIDAD 2

Comunicación

PRESENTATIONAL

3 PRESENTATIONAL WRITING

You are going to write a blog post to describe a family.

(Before writing)

A. Think about a fictional family you know (from a TV series, from a comic book, etc.).
Imagine that you are a member of that family.
Write a draft in your notebook, including the following information.

- ¿Cómo soy (físico y personalidad)?
- ¿Cómo es mi familia (miembros, nombres, parentesco, edad, mascotas, etc.)?
- ¿Cómo es cada miembro de la familia (físico y personalidad)?

(Write the post)

B. Introduce yourself and your family. You can make up the information.
Write at least four complete sentences.

(After writing)

C. Proofread before submitting your writing.
Correct any mistakes you may find.

- Have you used the vocabulary from the unit? Yes No
- Have you used the possessives correctly? Yes No
- Have you checked the noun-adjective agreement? Yes No

ESTRATEGIAS

Check your writing
Reading what you have written several times will help you correct your mistakes.

Comunicación

PRESENTATIONAL

4 PRESENTATIONAL SPEAKING

Imagine that you work for a film production company.
You are looking for two young actors and two young actresses to star in a teen movie.
You are going to record a radio advertisement to find possible candidates.

(Prepare the advertisement)

A. Write the script in your notebook.

> **1. Introduce** yourself and **say** what the goal
> of the ad is.
>
>> Me llamo... y soy...
>> Busco a...

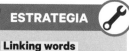

ESTRATEGIA

Linking words
Use **linking words** to
connect your ideas:
y, **porque**, **también**...

> **2. Describe** the physical appearance of the actors
> and the actresses you need: age, hair, eyes, height...
> **Write** two complete sentences to describe each person.
>
>> Busco a una muchacha...
>> Busco a un muchacho...

> **3. Add** a closing to your script.

(Practice and record yourself)

B. Practice several times.
Pay attention to your pronunciation—it will count toward your grade!
Repeat the words or sentences that are especially difficult for you.

C. Record your audio.
Make sure that you record it in a quiet place that is free from interruptions.

UNIDAD 2

Copyright © by Difusión, S. L.

Comunicación

INTERPERSONAL

5 **INTERPERSONAL WRITING**
You are going to write an email in reply to an advertisement.

(Read the advertisement)

A. What is *¡Baila en familia!*? ....

(Write the email)

B. Imagine that you and your family want to participate in the TV show.
Describe your family.
Say why you want to participate and why you think you are the perfect family for the show.
Give as many reasons as you can. Be creative!

CULTURE QUIZ

1 **Puerto Ricans...**

   a. are US citizens. ☐

   b. are not US citizens. ☐

2 **The Taino people used to live...**

   a. in Puerto Rico and other Caribbean islands. ☐

   b. in Puerto Rico and in some South American countries. ☐

3 **Select (✓) four sports that are very popular in Puerto Rico.**

   a. baseball ☐

   b. football ☐

   c. volleyball ☐

   d. basketball ☐

   e. boxing ☐

   f. car racing ☐

4 **La Borinqueña is the name of...**
(two options are correct)

   a. the Puerto Rican national anthem. ☐

   b. a fictional character. ☐

   c. a Puerto Rican animal. ☐

5 **Select (✓) two rhythms that are from Puerto Rico.**

   a. reggae ☐

   b. salsa ☐

   c. jazz ☐

   d. reggaeton ☐

   e. hip-hop ☐

   f. pop ☐

6 **The coquí...**

   a. only lives in Puerto Rico. ☐

   b. lives on many Caribbean islands. ☐

7 **Select (✓) four words that have Taino origin.**

   a. barbacoa ☐   **d.** caballo ☐

   b. canoa ☐   **e.** tortuga ☐

   c. hamaca ☐   **f.** iguana ☐

8 **How many family names do Puerto Ricans have?**

   a. One. ☐   **b.** Two. ☐   **c.** Three. ☐

9 **Street art...**

   a. is very important in Puerto Rico. ☐

   b. is not important in Puerto Rico. ☐

10 **Arturo Schomburg was a...**

   a. Puerto Rican baseball player. ☐

   b. Puerto Rican musician. ☐

   c. Puerto Rican historian. ☐

UNIDAD 2

UNIDAD

3 Hogar, dulce hogar

1 **A. Fill in** the chart about Mexico.

LOCALIZACIÓN	CIUDADES	COMIDA

LUGARES DE INTERÉS	OTROS

B. Watch the video.
Add new information to the chart.

Copyright © by Difusión, S. L.

Casas y apartamentos

LECCIÓN 1

MI VOCABULARIO

2 LAS PARTES DE LA CASA (1) • LA CASA

★ **Fill in** the gaps with the missing letters.

V E N T A N A

S C

R Z

P T

B Ó

A R T O

C

J Í

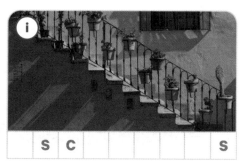

S C S

3 LAS PARTES DE LA CASA (1) • LA CASA

★★ **Underline** the correct option for each sentence.

a. En el apartamento hay **dos casas** / <u>**dos ventanas**</u> pequeñas.

b. Nosotros vivimos en **una casa** / **un apartamento** en el centro de la ciudad.

c. El apartamento tiene **una terraza** / **un patio**.

d. Me gusta mucho **el jardín** / **el apartamento** de tu casa.

e. **Las haciendas** / **Las terrazas** son casas tradicionales mexicanas.

f. La casa tiene un patio muy bonito con **unas escaleras** / **unas terrazas**.

UNIDAD 3

Casas y apartamentos

MI VOCABULARIO

4 LAS PARTES DE LA CASA (1) • LA CASA

★★★ **A. Look at** the pictures.

Write down any vocabulary that you recognize describing parts of a house.

La piscina, ...

🔊 **B. Listen to** Juan Carlos, Renata, and Juliana talking about their houses.

Underline where each of them lives.

Note that the houses are not all mentioned in the conversation.

1. Juan Carlos vive en **la casa a / la casa b / el apartamento c / la casa d**.

2. Renata vive en **la casa a / la casa b / el apartamento c / la casa d**.

3. Juliana vive en **la casa a / la casa b / el apartamento c / la casa d**.

Casas y apartamentos

MI GRAMÁTICA

5 RECUERDA: SER , TENER (IE), AND VIVIR

★★ **Complete** the dialogues with the correct form of **ser**, **tener**, or **vivir**.

a. ● Oye, Antonio. Y tú, ¿dónde .... *vives* .... ?

○ .... en el centro de Ciudad de México con mi familia.

b. ● ¿ .... (ustedes) en un apartamento o en una casa?

○ .... (nosotros) en un apartamento.

c. ● ¿Y cómo .... el apartamento?

○ .... muy grande y luminoso.

.... muchas ventanas y un balcón.

d. ● ¿ .... (ustedes) terraza en el apartamento?

○ No, no .... (nosotros) terraza,

pero el edificio .... una piscina comunitaria.

6 RECUERDA: QUANTIFIERS

★★ **Underline** the correct quantifier.

CASAS DE MÉXICO

A mí me gustan ^a**muy / <u>mucho</u>** las casas de mi país.
En el norte hay casas de adobe, que son ^b**muy / mucho**
agradables porque protegen del calor. También me
gustan ^c**muy / mucho** las haciendas, que son casas
coloniales ^d**muy / mucho** grandes. Normalmente tienen
jardines y patios. Ciudad de México es una ciudad
grande y ^e**muy / un poco** poblada, pero algunas (*some*) casas tienen patio.
Yo vivo en Ciudad de México. Mi casa es ^f**mucho / un poco** pequeña,
pero es ^g**muy / un poco** bonita y tiene un patio. El patio es un lugar
^h**muy / un poco** tranquilo.

UNIDAD 3

El apartamento nuevo

MI VOCABULARIO

7 **LAS PARTES DE LA CASA (1 Y 2)**

★ **Underline** the correct word for each illustration.

la ventana / el balcón / las escaleras

el jardín / la sala / el despacho

el patio / el comedor / la cocina

8 **LAS PARTES DE LA CASA (1 Y 2)**

★ **Circle** the six rooms that are indoors.

el jardín   el balcón   el baño   la sala   la habitación   el patio

la ventana   la cocina   la terraza   el despacho   el comedor

UNIDAD 3

9 **LAS PARTES DE LA CASA (2)**

★ **Fill in** the blanks with the correct rooms of the house.

a. el baño

b. ....

c. ....

d. ....

e. ....

f. ....

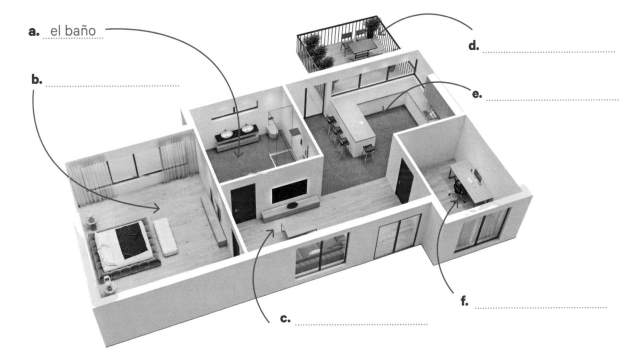

El apartamento nuevo

MI VOCABULARIO

10 LAS PARTES DE LA CASA (1 Y 2) • LOS MUEBLES Y LOS OBJETOS

★★ In what part of the house do you do these activities?

a. Trabajar con la computadora → ....

b. Ver la televisión ──────→ ....

c. Jugar al béisbol ──────→ ....

d. Comer ──────────→ ....

11 LAS PARTES DE LA CASA (1 Y 2) • LOS MUEBLES Y LOS OBJETOS

★ **Classify** the words in the correct column.

a. ~~el armario~~

b. el refrigerador

c. la cama

d. el baño

e. el sofá

f. la habitación

g. el jardín

h. el espejo

i. la ducha

j. el despacho

k. la cocina

l. la sala

MUEBLES Y OTROS OBJETOS	PARTES DE LA CASA
el armario, ...	

12 DESCRIBIR UN ESPACIO

★★★ **Complete** the sentences with the words below.

pequeña   grande   nueva   vieja   luminosa   oscura   ~~bonito~~   fea

a. Me gusta el sofá de tu casa. Es muy ....bonito.....

b. La cocina de mi casa es un poco .... No hay ventanas.

c. La terraza es .... Hay plantas, una mesa, cuatro sillas y un sofá.

d. Me gusta mucho estar en la sala porque hay mucho sol. Es muy ....

e. Mi cama es un poco .... Tiene muchos años.

f. Tengo una mesa .... Es la primera vez (the first time) que la uso.

g. No me gusta la decoración de la cocina, y, además, no hay espacio:

es .... y ....

UNIDAD 3

El apartamento nuevo

MI GRAMÁTICA

13 **EXPRESSING EXISTENCE WITH** HAY

★★ **Underline** the correct option to best complete the sentence.
Note that Ø means "no word".

a. En mi casa no hay **Ø** / **el** jardín. ⟶

b. ¿En tu apartamento hay **Ø** / **la** terraza? ⟶

c. En el comedor hay **Ø** / **una** silla muy bonita. ⟶

d. En nuestra casa no hay **Ø** / **una** piscina. ⟶

e. En el baño no hay **Ø** / **unas** ventanas. ⟶

14 **EXPRESSING EXISTENCE WITH** HAY • **RECUERDA:** TENER (IE) **AND** SER

★★ **Complete** the sentences with **es**, **hay**, or **tiene**.

a. En mi casa no ....hay.... piscina.

b. Mi habitación .... dos camas.

c. .... un sofá grande en la sala de mi casa.

d. Mi casa no .... nueva, pero .... muy bonita.

e. La cocina de mi casa no .... ventanas.

f. El despacho de mi casa .... un poco pequeño.

15 **EXPRESSING EXISTENCE WITH** HAY

★★★ Do you have these objects in your kitchen?
Write complete sentences that are true for you.

a. refrigerador → En la cocina de mi casa hay / no hay un refrigerador. ....

b. sillas → ....

c. escaleras → ....

d. estantería → ....

e. sofá → ....

UNIDAD 3

¿Dónde están mis cosas?

MI VOCABULARIO

16 LOS MUEBLES Y LOS OBJETOS • LAS PARTES DE LA CASA (2)

★★ **A. Look at** the illustration.

Match the words below (**1–9**) with the corresponding object in the illustration (**a–i**).

1. la estantería `b`

2. la mesa ☐

3. la planta ☐

4. el cuadro ☐

5. la ventana ☐

6. la lámpara ☐

7. el televisor ☐

8. el sofá ☐

9. la pared ☐

B. What room of the house is this?

Es ....

17 LOS MUEBLES Y LOS OBJETOS • LAS PARTES DE LA CASA (2)

★ What objects and pieces of furniture do you associate with these rooms?
Write at least four different words for each room.

LA COCINA	EL BAÑO	LA HABITACIÓN
la estufa		

UNIDAD 3

¿Dónde están mis cosas?

MI VOCABULARIO

18 **LOS MUEBLES Y LOS OBJETOS**
★★ **Find** the odd one out in each series.

a. el sofá | la estantería | ~~la ducha~~ | el televisor

b. la ducha | el inodoro | el refrigerador | el lavamanos

c. el refrigerador | la cama | la estufa | el armario

d. la cama | el inodoro | la estantería | el cuadro

e. el espejo | la ducha | el lavamanos | la estufa

19 **LOS MUEBLES Y LOS OBJETOS**
★★ **Describe** the room, including furniture, objects, size, and decor.
Say if you like it or not, and **explain** why.

ESTRATEGIA 🔧

Write Post-it notes

It might be a good moment to fill your house or your room with Post-it notes with the **Spanish words for the objects and places** you have learned in this lesson.

En la sala hay...

....

....

....

....

....

UNIDAD 3

¿Dónde están mis cosas?

MI GRAMÁTICA

20 PREPOSITIONS OF PLACE

★★ **Look at** the illustration.
Complete the sentences below with the corresponding preposition.
Write del when necessary.

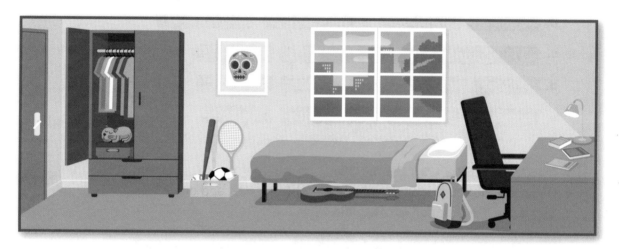

delante de   detrás de   al lado de   encima de   debajo de   dentro de   ~~en~~

a. El cuadro está .... en .... la pared.

b. La guitarra está .... la cama.

c. La mochila está .... la silla.

d. Los libros están .... la mesa.

e. El gato está .... el armario.

f. La mesa está .... la silla.

g. La caja está .... el armario.

ESTRATEGIA

Memorize grammar

To memorize these prepositions, you can **write sentences about your own bedroom** like the ones in activity 20. Use a different color to highlight the prepositions.

21 EXPRESSING LOCATION WITH ESTAR • PREPOSITION OF PLACE

★★ **Say** where these objects and furniture are in your classroom.
Write complete sentences, conjugating **estar** in the correct form.

a. Mi mesa está al lado de... ....

b. Los libros ....

c. La puerta ....

d. El pizarrón ....

UNIDAD 3

Estilo mexicano

MI VOCABULARIO

22 LOS COLORES

★★ What colors are these things?

Remember, the adjectives must agree in number and gender with the noun described.

 a. El sol es _____ amarillo. _____

 b. Los tomates son _____

 c. Las plantas son _____

 d. Las naranjas son _____

 e. El cielo es _____

 f. La tierra es _____

 g. La leche es _____

 h. Mi color favorito es el _____

23 LOS COLORES

★★ **Read** the description of the room.

Color the illustration according to the description.

🔊

Me encanta mi habitación: es muy colorida. La cama es marrón y la ropa de la cama (*bedding*) es verde. Al lado de la cama, hay una mesa pequeña anaranjada con una lámpara amarilla. La mesa donde estudio es roja, y la silla es gris y negra. La ventana es de color morado. El armario tiene dos colores: rojo y rosa.

Y la puerta es color rosa mexicano. ¿Qué te parece? (*What do you think?*)

¡Por suerte (*luckily*), las paredes son blancas!

UNIDAD 3

Estilo mexicano

LECCIÓN 1

MI VOCABULARIO

24 **LA DECORACIÓN • LOS MATERIALES**

★★ **Complete** the crossword puzzle with the words for these objects or materials.

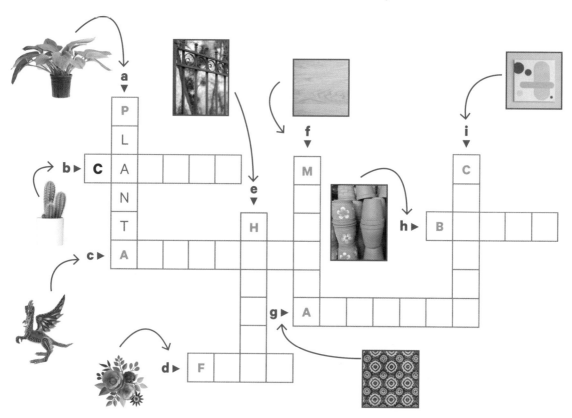

25 **LA DECORACIÓN • LOS MATERIALES**

★★★**Describe** the kitchen in the picture.
Mention the materials, colors, and decor.
Write complete sentences.

Hay una mesa...

....

....

....

....

....

....

....

UNIDAD 3

Estilo mexicano
LECCIÓN 1

MI GRAMÁTICA

26 RECUERDA: EXPRESSING LOCATION WITH ESTAR
★★ **Underline** the correct verb.

> Mi apartamento ᵃ**es / está** en Ciudad de México. ᵇ**Es / Está** un poco pequeño, pero ᶜ**es / está** muy luminoso. Mi habitación ᵈ**es / está** al lado de la sala. Me gusta mucho porque ᵉ**es / está** muy colorida y original. Las paredes ᶠ**son / están** verdes, y la puerta ᵍ**es / está** naranja. Tengo dos alebrijes muy bonitos. ʰ**Son / Están** en una estantería.

27 RECUERDA: PREPOSITION OF PLACE
★★ **Listen to** the description.
🔊 **Draw** the missing elements in the correct place.

ESTRATEGIA

Make predictions
Before listening to the audio, it would be useful to **look at the picture and try ro remember the names of the objects and furniture** you see.

UNIDAD 3

Copyright © by Difusión, S. L.

Comunicación

1 INTERPRETIVE READING

You are going to read two advertisements from a Mexican real estate website.

Apartamento en Ciudad de México

Es un apartamento muy bonito de dos habitaciones. Una habitación tiene una cama grande y la otra habitación tiene dos camas. El apartamento tiene un baño completo, un comedor y una sala muy luminosa con terraza. También tiene una cocina con todo lo necesario para cocinar.

Servicios incluidos
Wi-Fi
Elevador

Servicios no incluidos
Garaje

50 evaluaciones:

Francisco Javier
El apartamento es práctico y muy luminoso, pero las habitaciones son un poco pequeñas.

Ana Lucía
El apartamento es muy bonito. Es nuevo y está en el centro de la ciudad.

Casa con piscina en Morelos

Es una casa espectacular en las afueras (suburbs). Es ideal para estar en contacto con la naturaleza (nature). Tiene tres habitaciones, tres baños, una cocina con un comedor, una sala y un jardín muy grande con piscina privada. Las mascotas son bienvenidas.

Servicios incluidos
Garaje

Servicios no incluidos
Wi-Fi
Elevador

50 evaluaciones:

Jorge Iván
Es muy bonita y moderna, pero no es muy práctica porque tiene muchas escaleras.

Sofía
La piscina es un poco pequeña, pero la casa es muy bonita y el jardín es increíble.

UNIDAD 3

(Before reading)

A. Look at at the pictures on the previous page.
Which option do you like the most? Why?

....

....

(First reading)

B. Match each sentence with the correct advertisement.
Select el apartamento (**A**) or la casa (**C**).

1. Tiene dos habitaciones. A C

2. Es muy grande. A C

3. Tiene muchas escaleras. A C

4. Tiene un garaje. A C

5. Tiene tres habitaciones. A C

6. Tiene muchos baños. A C

7. Las habitaciones son pequeñas. A C

8. Está en el centro. A C

(Second reading)

C. Decide which house suits these people best.
Explain why.

La mejor *(best)* opción para ellos es... ....

...., porque...

....

....

....

La mejor *(best)* opción para ellos es... ....

...., porque...

....

....

....

Comunicación

INTERPRETIVE

2 **INTERPRETIVE LISTENING**

You are going to listen to a phone conversation between Carlos and his mom.

(Before listening)

A. Think about a house in the suburbs.
Write five words that you associate with this type of house.

....

....

....

(First listen)

B. Focus on the gist of what is being said.
What do they talk about?

1. Hablan de su casa nueva. ☐

2. Hablan de la casa de un amigo de Carlos. ☐

3. Hablan de su apartamento. ☐

ESTRATEGIA 🔧

Get the gist

Don't panic if you don't understand everything. **Focus on identifying key words** to help you understand the main idea.

(Second listen)

C. Focus on the details.
What parts of the house do they mention?

1. las habitaciones ☐	**4.** la piscina ☐	**7.** la terraza ☐
2. la cocina ☐	**5.** el comedor ☐	**8.** el jardín ☐
3. la sala ☐	**6.** el baño ☐	**9.** el patio ☐

D. What is there in the garden?

....

(After listening)

E. Write two complete sentences to describe the house.

....

....

UNIDAD 3

Comunicación

PRESENTATIONAL

3 **PRESENTATIONAL WRITING**

Imagine that you have just moved to a new home.
You are going to write an email to a friend.

(Write the email)

A. Answer the questions below in complete sentences.

- ¿Es una casa o un apartamento?
- ¿Cuántas habitaciones tiene? ¿Cómo son?
- Describe dónde están algunos *(some)* muebles y objetos.

Hola, ¿qué tal?

Ahora vivo en...

....

....

....

....

....

....

....

....

....

....

Enviar

(After writing)

B. Read your email again.
Correct any mistakes you may find.

- Have you used the verbs **estar** and **haber** correctly? | Yes | No |
- Have you used the correct prepositions of place? | Yes | No |
- Have you used the vocabulary from the unit? | Yes | No |

UNIDAD 3

Comunicación

PRESENTATIONAL

4 **PRESENTATIONAL SPEAKING**
Imagine that you are a vlogger.
You are going to record a house tour.
It can be a real house or an invented one.

(Prepare the video)

A. Write the script in your notebook.

1. **Say** if it is a house or an apartment.

    Vivo en…

2. **Present** the parts of the house.
   Describe them and **say** where they are located.

    La cocina es muy grande y…
    El baño está al lado de la cocina…

3. **Describe** five pieces of furniture and five objects,
   mentioning colors and size.

    En la sala, hay una silla de madera…

4. **Add** a greeting and a closing to your script.

(Practice and record yourself)

B. Practice several times.
   Pay attention to your pronunciation—it will count toward your grade!
   Repeat the words or sentences that are especially difficult for you.

C. Record your video.
   Make sure that you record in a quiet place
   that is free from interruptions.

ESTRATEGIAS 🔧

Check the recording
Do you sound **clear
and natural**? Is it easy
to understand you?
Checking your work
is really important in
helping you to improve
your speaking skills.

UNIDAD 3

Comunicación

INTERPERSONAL

5 **INTERPERSONAL WRITING**

You are going to reply to Guadalupe's latest social media post.

(Read Guadalupe's post)

A. Which room of her house is she talking about? ....

Guadalupe
Me gusta mucho la sala de mi casa nueva. Estudio en la sala porque es muy luminosa y hay mucho espacio. Además, en la sala escucho música en el equipo de mis papás. ¡Me ayuda a concentrarme!
Y ustedes, ¿dónde estudian?

(Write the comment)

B. Reply to Guadalupe's question.
Ask her some questions about her house.

Responder a Guadalupe

....
....
....
....
....
....
....
....
....

(After writing)

C. Proofread before submitting your work.
Correct any mistakes you may find.

- Have you included everything you were asked for? [Yes] [No]

- Have you written complete sentences? [Yes] [No]

ESTRATEGIAS

Using the dictionary wisely

You can use the dictionary to find words you don't know. However, try to make an effort to remember **all the vocabulary you have learned so far.**

Hogares chicanos

MI VOCABULARIO

1 **DESCRIBIR UN ESPACIO**

★★ **A. Look at** the pictures.

Put a mark (✓) in the column under the bedroom that is described in each sentence.

la habitación de Eva

la habitación de Sarah

	LA HABITACIÓN DE EVA	LA HABITACIÓN DE SARAH
1. Es grande y luminosa.		✓
2. Está muy desordenada.		
3. Está limpia.		
4. Hay un balcón.		
5. Está sucia.		
6. Hay una computadora encima de la cama.		
7. Está muy ordenada.		
8. No hay balcón.		
9. Es un poco pequeña.		

B. Write two more complete sentences for each bedroom.

La habitación de Eva es...

....

El habitación de Sarah es...

....

Hogares chicanos

MI VOCABULARIO

2 DESCRIBIR UN ESPACIO
★ **Write** the opposite of these adjectives.

a. bonito / bonita ⟶ ....feo........ / ....fea........

b. limpio / limpia ⟶ .... / ....

c. ordenado / ordenada → .... / ....

d. tradicional ⟶ .... / ....

e. luminoso / luminosa → .... / ....

f. grande ⟶ .... / ....

g. nuevo / nueva ⟶ .... / ....

ESTRATEGIA

Personalize to memorize
Select the adjectives that describe your own house or bedroom. Think of other houses and bedrooms you know and select the appropriate adjectives. **Create a mind map** with categories like "my bedroom," "Tony's bedroom," "Grandma's house"…

3 DESCRIBIR UN ESPACIO
★★★ **Describe** this bedroom with some of the adjectives below.
Make sure you use **ser** and **estar** correctly.

moderna
tradicional
ordenada
desordenada
luminosa
oscura
limpia
sucia

UNIDAD 3

Copyright © by Difusión, S. L.

a. La habitación es... ....

b. La habitación está... ....

Hogares chicanos

MI GRAMÁTICA

4 **SER** AND **ESTAR** TO DESCRIBE

★★ **A. Read** these comments from a Mexican magazine for teenagers.
Underline the correct answer.

(1) **AJ dijo...**

Mi habitación ª**es** / **está** grande y muy luminosa porque hay dos ventanas. Las paredes
ᵇ**son** / **están** blancas y hay varios objetos de color rosa y azul, mis colores favoritos.
Hay una cama que también ᶜ**es** / **está** un sofá. También hay una mesa, una silla y dos
cuadros. Mi habitación siempre ᵈ**es** / **está** limpia y ordenada.

(2) **T15 dijo...**

En mi habitación hay una cama, una mesa, estanterías y una silla. Las paredes
ª**son** / **están** de color blanco. Mi habitación ᵇ**es** / **está** pequeña, pero ᶜ**es** / **está**
luminosa porque hay dos ventanas: una grande y una pequeña. A mí me gusta mucho,
pero a veces ᵈ**es** / **está** un poco desordenada.

B. Which of the comments is a description of this picture?

(1) ☐

(2) ☐

5 **SER** AND **ESTAR** TO DESCRIBE

★★★ **Write** a description of your bedroom for the magazine from activity 4.
Make sure you use **ser** and **estar** correctly.

Mi habitación es / está...

....

....

....

....

UNIDAD 3

Tengo que hacer la cama

● **MI VOCABULARIO**

6 **LOS QUEHACERES (1)**

★ **A. Listen to** the voice message.

🔊 **Put a mark** (✓) in the box for the household chores Eduardo has to do today.

B. Listen to the voice message again.

Write which household chores Eduardo has to do today.

Eduardo tiene que... ....

....

....

....

UNIDAD 3

Tengo que hacer la cama

MI VOCABULARIO

7 **LOS QUEHACERES (1)**

★ **Complete** the phrases with a verb.
Only one of them has more than one correct verb option.

a. _____hacer_____ la cama

b. _____ los platos

c. _____ la mesa

d. _____ la basura

e. _____ la habitación

f. _____ a pasear al perro

8 **LOS QUEHACERES (1)**

★★ **Look at** the illustrations.
Put a mark (✓) in the box beside each of the household chores that must be done.

Jorge tiene que...

1. hacer la cama. ☐

2. poner la mesa. ☐

3. sacar a pasear al perro. ☐

4. ordenar la habitación. ☐

5. quitar la mesa. ☐

6. lavar los platos. ☐

La familia Torrejón tiene que...

1. lavar los platos. ☐

2. poner la mesa. ☐

3. quitar la mesa. ☐

4. sacar la basura. ☐

5. sacar a pasear al perro. ☐

6. hacer la cama. ☐

UNIDAD 3

Tengo que hacer la cama ▬▬▬▬▬▬▬▬▬▬▬ LECCIÓN 2

● MI GRAMÁTICA

⑨ TENER QUE (IE) + INFINITIVE

★★ **Complete** the sentences below with the correct form of either **tener que** or **tener**.

a. Hoy estoy ocupado: ....*tengo que*.... ordenar mi habitación.

b. ● Carlos, ¿tú .... hermanos?

   ○ Sí, ... dos, un hermano y una hermana.

c. Mi hermana .... muchos amigos de origen mexicano.

d. Mi hermano y yo .... sacar a pasear al perro todos los días.

e. Hoy Luis y Maya .... poner la mesa.

⑩ ADVERBS OF FREQUENCY

★★ **Look at** Emma Sofía's household chore list.
Use the adverbs of frequency below to say how often Emma Sofía has to do each chore.
More than one option is possible for some sentences.

	LUNES	MARTES	MIÉRCOLES	JUEVES	VIERNES
a. hacer la cama	✓	✓	✓	✓	✓
b. ordenar la habitación				✓	
c. poner la mesa	✓		✓		✓
d. quitar la mesa		✓		✓	
e. lavar los platos	✓	✓		✓	✓
f. sacar la basura					

[todos los días] [... veces por semana] [casi nunca] [nunca] [a menudo]

a. Emma Sofía tiene que hacer la cama todos los días. ....

b. ....

c. ....

d. ....

e. ....

f. ....

UNIDAD 3

¿Qué haces en casa?

MI VOCABULARIO

11 **LOS QUEHACERES (1 Y 2)**

★ **Look at** this Mexican family's household chore list.

Say what each person does on Saturday.

SÁBADO

Juan

Esmeralda (hermana de Juan)

Nieves (mamá de Juan y Esmeralda)

Luis Miguel (papá de Juan y Esmeralda)

a. El sábado, Juan hace la cama, ...
....
....

b. ....
....
....

c. ....
....

d. ....
....

¿Qué haces en casa?

● **MI VOCABULARIO**

12 LOS QUEHACERES (1 Y 2)
★★ **Match** each verb (**a–i**) with the noun (**1–9**) that takes the verb's action.

a. lavar	**1.** al perro
b. ordenar	**2.** el césped
c. poner y quitar	**3.** la lavadora
d. sacar	**4.** los platos
e. hacer	**5.** la mesa
f. cortar	**6.** la compra
g. sacar a pasear	**7.** la basura
h. poner	**8.** la habitación
i. pasar	**9.** la aspiradora

● **13 LOS QUEHACERES (1 Y 2)**
★★★ **Complete** the sentences with two household chores.

a. Yo siempre... ....

b. Yo a menudo... ....

c. Yo a veces... ....

● **d.** Yo casi nunca... ....

e. Yo nunca... ....

UNIDAD 3

¿Qué haces en casa?

LECCIÓN 2

MI GRAMÁTICA

14 IRREGULAR YO FORM: PONER AND HACER • RECUERDA: TENER (E > IE)
★★ **Read** the sentences. Who does these household chores?
Put a mark (✓) in the box to show which person does each chore.

	YO	MI PAPÁ	MIS HERMANOS
a. Hago la cama todos los días.	✓		
b. Tienen que ordenar su habitación.			
c. Pone la lavadora dos días por semana.			
d. A veces tengo que sacar la basura.			
e. Hace la compra los sábados.			
f. Siempre pongo la mesa.			
g. Nunca hacen la compra.			
h. Tiene que planchar todas las semanas.			

15 IRREGULAR YO FORM • RECUERDA: ADVERBS OF FREQUENCY
★★★ **Write** complete sentences using the words below.

a. Sara | nunca | ordenar su habitación

→ Sara nunca ordena su habitación.

b. Mi hermano | siempre | hacer la cama

→ ....

c. Yo | casi nunca | hacer la compra

→ ....

d. Mi hermano y yo | nunca | planchar

→ ....

e. Yo | a veces | cocinar

→ ....

f. Mi papá | todos los días | poner la mesa

→ ....

Reporteros 1

Vivir y convivir

MI VOCABULARIO

16 **CONVIVIR (1 Y 2)**

★★ **A. Say** how many hours you do housework every week.
Write a complete sentence.

Yo hago...

....

....

B. Do you think you share enough responsibilities at home?
Explain why or why not.

Yo (no) comparto...

....

....

17 **CONVIVIR (1 Y 2)**

★★ **Say** how often you do these things.
Give an example.
Use the adverbs of frequency below.

| siempre | casi siempre | a menudo | a veces | casi nunca | nunca |

a. Ayudar a tus papás o hermanos.

Yo (no) ayudo...

Por ejemplo,

b. Compartir tus cosas con tu familia.

....

Por ejemplo,

c. Pasar tiempo con tu familia.

....

Por ejemplo,

d. Poner excusas para no hacer tus quehaceres.

....

Por ejemplo,

UNIDAD 3

Vivir y convivir

LECCIÓN 2

MI VOCABULARIO

18 **CONVIVIR (1 Y 2) • RECUERDA: LOS QUEHACERES**
★★ **Complete** this blog post with the correct forms of the following verbs.

> hacer | compartir (x3) | pasar | poner | ayudar | quitar | convivir | sacar | lavar

MI VIDA EN CASA

Yo vivo con mis papás y mi hermano Ricardo en una casa en las Lomas
de Anáhuac, en Monterrey. La casa no es muy grande, y mi hermano
y yo ^a __compartimos__ la habitación. ¡También ^b _____
los amigos! ^c _____ mucho tiempo juntos, pero no hay
problemas entre nosotros.

Somos una familia que ^d _____ responsabilidades.
Mi mamá siempre ^e _____ los platos. Mi papá siempre
^f _____ la compra y cocina. También limpia el baño
y casi siempre ordena la casa. Yo siempre ^g _____
y ^h _____ la mesa y casi siempre ^i _____
la basura porque a veces mi hermano pone excusas y no lo hace. Pero él casi
siempre ^j _____ a mi papá a cocinar porque le gusta mucho.

Ya lo ven, en mi familia ^k _____ en paz y armonía.

Vivir y convivir

MI GRAMÁTICA

19 **RECUERDA: IRREGULAR YO FORM • RECUERDA: REGULAR VERBS**
★★ Sergio, Mateo, and Virginia are siblings.
Complete their conversation using the correct form of the verb in parentheses.

Sergio

Muchachos, **(tener, nosotros)** [a] __tenemos__ que decidir
quién hace los quehaceres de la lista de mamá.

Mateo

Okey, yo **(lavar)** [b] .... los platos. ¡Me gusta!

Sergio

¡Perfecto! Pues yo **(pasar)** [c] .... la aspiradora.
Virginia, ¿tú **(sacar)** [d] .... la basura?

Virginia

¡Ay, no! No me gusta sacar la basura.
Si ustedes **(sacar)** [e] .... la basura,
yo **(hacer)** [f] .... la compra.

Sergio

Mmm... Bueno, de acuerdo. Si tú **(hacer)** [g] ....
la compra, yo **(sacar)** [h] .... la basura, ¿okey?

Virginia

Okey. Mateo, ¿tú **(poner)** [i] .... la mesa?

Mateo

Sí, yo **(poner)** [j] .... y **(quitar)**
[k] .... la mesa.

Sergio

¡Genial! Y todos **(ordenar)** [l] .... nuestras
habitaciones, **(hacer)** [m] .... nuestras camas,
¿de acuerdo?

UNIDAD 3

Comunicación

INTERPRETIVE

1 **INTERPRETIVE READING**

You are going to read a blog post from a volunteering website.

UNA EXPERIENCIA MUY BONITA

Me llamo Brice, vivo en Houston y estudio español en la escuela. Para practicar español, hago un voluntariado con una pareja de ancianos de origen mexicano: doña Fina y don Joaquín.

En el voluntariado, hago quehaceres para ellos: hago la compra dos veces por
5 semana y a veces ayudo a don Joaquín a hacer reparaciones. También saco a pasear a Choco, su perra. Doña Fina cocina todos los días y, a veces, cocino con ella. ¡Hacemos tacos y burritos deliciosos! A don Joaquín no le gusta cocinar y siempre pone excusas para no entrar en la cocina.

Doña Fina y don Joaquín tienen un apartamento pequeño, pero siempre está
10 muy ordenado y limpio. Doña Fina pasa la aspiradora y ordena todos los días. Don Joaquín siempre saca la basura. Él cree que comparte las responsabilidades en casa de manera igualitaria, ¡ja, ja, ja!

Me gusta mucho pasar tiempo con ellos. Aprendo curiosidades de México y practico español. ¡Es una experiencia muy bonita!

(Before reading)

A. Write two things you can do if you volunteer with the elderly.

Puedo ayudar a...

(First reading)

B. Answer the questions in complete sentences.

1. ¿Por qué hace Brice el voluntariado? Brice hace el voluntariado para...

2. ¿Qué hace en el voluntariado?

3. ¿Cómo es el apartamento de doña Fina y don Joaquín?

4. ¿Le gusta la experiencia? ¿Por qué?

UNIDAD 3

(Second reading)

C. Put a mark (✓) in the box to show which person does each of the following chores.

	DOÑA FINA	DON JOAQUÍN	BRICE
hacer la compra			
hacer reparaciones			
sacar a pasear a Choco			
cocinar			
pasar la aspiradora			
ordenar el apartamento			
sacar la basura			

(After reading)

D. Do doña Fina and don Joaquín share responsibilities at home? Why?

Comunicación

LECCIÓN 2

INTERPRETIVE

2 **INTERPRETIVE LISTENING** 🔊

You are going to listen to Jenny and María Luisa's conversation.

(Before listening)

A. Read the **Cultura** box.

What are the advantages of being an *au pair*?

....

....

> **CULTURA**
>
> Un *au pair* es una persona joven que vive en un país extranjero con una familia de acogida *(host family)*. Normalmente, su trabajo consiste en estar con los hijos pequeños y hacer quehaceres ligeros *(light)*. A cambio *(In exchange)*, el o la *au pair* aprende un idioma y convive con la familia.

🔊 (First listen)

B. Listen for the gist of what is said.

What are Jenny and María Luisa talking about?

Put a mark (✓) in the topics they discuss.

1. Los quehaceres ☐ 　　**4.** Los idiomas que habla Jenny ☐

2. La casa ☐ 　　**5.** La familia ☐

3. El salario del trabajo ☐ 　　**6.** La ciudad ☐

🔊 (Second listen)

C. Decide whether the following sentences are true (**T**) or false (**F**).
Correct the false sentences.

1. María Luisa tiene dos hijos. ☐T ☐F

....

2. Jenny tiene que estar con los niños. ☐T ☐F

....

3. Jenny tiene que practicar inglés. ☐T ☐F

....

4. Jenny tiene que trabajar los fines de semana. ☐T ☐F

....

5. El salario es de cincuenta pesos por semana. ☐T ☐F

....

UNIDAD 3

Comunicación

PRESENTATIONAL

3 **PRESENTATIONAL WRITING**

Imagine you are participating in an exchange program where you live with a Mexican family. You are going to write a blog post about the experience.

(Before writing)

A. Imagine the situation.

Write a draft in your notebook, including the following information:

• ¿Cómo es la familia (nombres, edades, etc.)? ¿Tienen mascotas?

• ¿Cómo es la casa?

• ¿Tienes que compartir habitación?

• ¿Cuáles quehaceres tienes que hacer?

(Write the blog post)

B. You should write at least four complete sentences.

....

....

....

....

....

....

....

....

....

....

(After writing)

C. Proofread the blog post.

Correct any mistakes you may find.

ESTRATEGIA

Proofread your writing
Proofread your writing several times. You can **avoid making mistakes** by doing so.

• Have you used the vocabulary from the unit? | Yes | No |

• Have you used **ser** and **estar** correctly? | Yes | No |

• Have you conjugated **hacer**, **poner**, and **tener que** correctly? | Yes | No |

• Are your sentences easy to understand? | Yes | No |

UNIDAD 3

Comunicación

PRESENTATIONAL

4 **PRESENTATIONAL SPEAKING**

A Mexican radio program is inviting their listeners to describe their bedrooms. You are going to record a voice message for the program.

(Prepare the voice message)

A. Write the script in your notebook.

1. Describe your bedroom, including: furniture, objects, decor, and whether or not you share it.

Mi habitación es...
En mi habitación hay...

2. Say if the bedroom is tidy or untidy.

La cama está...

3. Say what household chores you need to do in your bedroom and how often.

Tengo que...

4. Add a greeting and a closing.

(Practice and record yourself)

B. Rehearse several times and **record** your voice message.

C. Listen to the recording.
- Is the sound clear? Yes No
- Can you improve your pronunciation? Yes No
- Is your intonation clear? Yes No

D. If needed, **record** the message again.

UNIDAD 3

Comunicación

INTERPERSONAL

5 INTERPERSONAL WRITING
Imagine that you have a friend in Mexico.
You are going to reply to one of his emails.

(Read the email)

A. Circle in blue Mariano's problem.
Circle in green what questions he asks you.

Hola, ¿qué tal?

Tengo que ordenar mi habitación. Mis papás dicen que está muy desordenada
y sucia, pero yo la veo bien.

En mi familia compartimos los quehaceres. Todos los días mi papá cocina
y mi mamá lava los platos. Mi hermana Laura siempre pone y quita la mesa, y yo
saco la basura. Somos muy organizados. Los fines de semana, mi mamá hace
la compra y mi papá limpia la casa. Y... mi hermana y yo tenemos que ordenar
nuestras habitaciones. ¡Pero yo tengo mucho trabajo y no me gusta ordenar!

Y en tu casa, ¿comparten los quehaceres? ¿Qué tiene que hacer cada uno?
¿Tienen que hacer quehaceres que no les gustan?

Un abrazo,

Mariano

(Reply to Mariano's email)

B. Answer Mariano's questions.
Mention his problem and **say** if you have a similar one or not.

....

....

....

....

....

....

UNIDAD 3

CULTURE QUIZ

1 **¿Cuál es el país hispanoamericano con más población?**

a. ▮▮ Perú. ☐

b. ▮•▮ México. ☐

c. ▙▬ Chile. ☐

2 **México está en...**

a. Europa. ☐

b. América del Sur. ☐

c. América del Norte. ☐

3 **La capital de México es...**

a. Puebla. ☐

b. Ciudad de México. ☐

c. Tijuana. ☐

4 **¿Cuál de estos idiomas es de México?**

a. El náhuatl. ☐

b. El catalán. ☐

c. El quechua. ☐

5 **Quetzalcóatl es...**

a. un pájaro centroamericano. ☐

b. una serpiente centroamericana. ☐

c. un dios centroamericano. ☐

6 **"Parte de los Estados Unidos fue (was) territorio mexicano en el pasado".**

a. Verdadero. ☐

b. Falso. ☐

7 **¿Qué es La Casa Azul?**

a. Es un museo de arte clásico mexicano. ☐

b. Es la casa-museo de Frida Kahlo. ☐

c. Es un apartamento famoso de Coyoacán. ☐

8 **¿Qué significa "chicano/a"?**

a. Persona estadounidense de origen mexicano. ☐

b. Persona mexicana de origen estadounidense. ☐

c. Persona estadounidense de origen chileno. ☐

9 **Los alebrijes son...**

a. unos pájaros típicos de México. ☐

b. unos objetos típicos de artesanía mexicana. ☐

10 **¿Cuál de estas ciudades NO está en México?**

a. Guadalajara. ☐

b. Buenos Aires. ☐

c. Monterrey. ☐

UNIDAD 3

UNIDAD 4

Un colegio para todo el mundo

¿Qué más pues?
Soy **Juan José**,
de Bogotá.

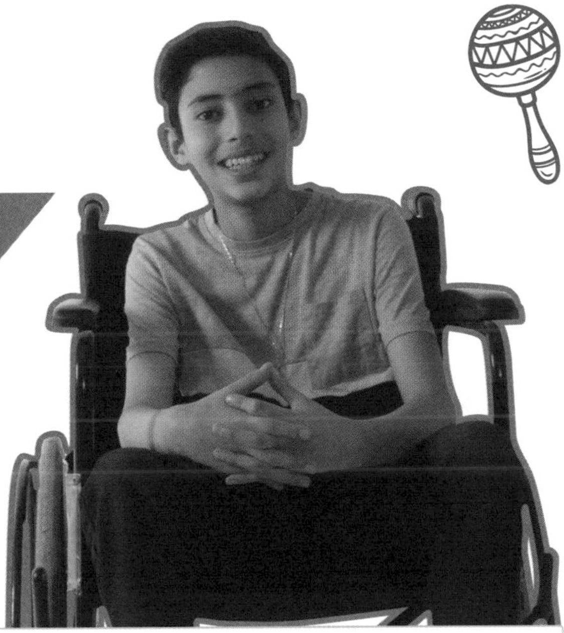

1 **A. Look at** the picture and **read** the information.
Where is Juan José from?

....

B. Watch the video.
What does he like the most about his country?

....

....

....

C. Write the name of:

1. una ciudad colonial → ....

2. un/a artista → ....

3. un escritor → ....

4. un deportista → ....

Copyright © by Difusión, S. L.

Las partes del colegio

LECCIÓN 1

MI VOCABULARIO

2 LAS PARTES DEL COLEGIO

★ **Fill in** the blanks below with the term for each school area shown.

| la entrada | la biblioteca | el gimnasio | el salón de computadoras |

| la cafetería | el patio | el salón de clase | la cancha de deporte |

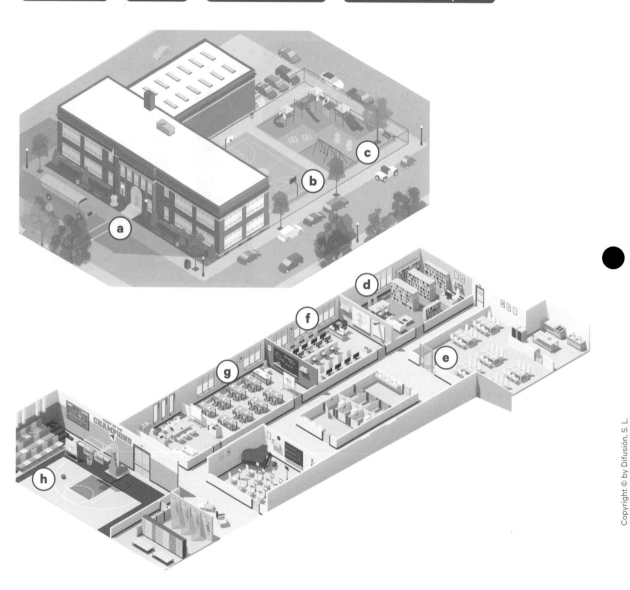

UNIDAD 4

a. la entrada ....

b. ....

c. ....

d. ....

e. ....

f. ....

g. ....

h. ....

Reporteros 1

Las partes del colegio

MI VOCABULARIO

3 **LAS PARTES DEL COLEGIO**

★ **Write** the correct words under each picture.

el laboratorio | la oficina del / de la director/a | el auditorio | la secretaría

4 **LAS PARTES DEL COLEGIO**

★★ Where do these things usually take place? **Answer** the questions.

¿Cuál es el lugar *(place)* donde...

a. estás durante el recreo? El patio. ....

b. estudias y lees libros? ....

c. haces Educación Física dentro del colegio? ....

d. almuerzas? ....

e. está normalmente el / la director/a? ....

f. haces experimentos de ciencias? ....

g. haces deporte al aire libre *(outdoors)*? ....

h. usas una computadora? ....

UNIDAD 4

Las partes del colegio

MI GRAMÁTICA

5 **RECUERDA: PREPOSITIONS OF PLACE**

★ **Look at** the illustration.
Complete the sentences below with **del** or **de la**.

a. El patio está delante .... auditorio.

b. La oficina de la directora está delante .... entrada.

c. El salón de computadoras está al lado .... biblioteca.

d. El auditorio está al lado .... baño.

6 **RECUERDA: TAMBIÉN , TAMPOCO , SÍ , NO**

★ **Complete** the sentences with **también**, **tampoco**, **sí**, or **no**.

a. • ¿Ustedes tienen auditorio en su colegio? Nosotros sí.

o Nosotros .... Mi colegio es pequeño y no hay espacio para un auditorio.

b. • En mi colegio no tenemos piscina.

o En mi colegio .... Tenemos que ir al centro deportivo municipal.

c. • En nuestro colegio no tenemos salón de computadoras.

o En mi colegio .... ¡Y tenemos muchas computadoras!

d. • En mi colegio tenemos un salón para cada grupo. ¿Y en tu colegio?

o En mi colegio .... Y además, tenemos un laboratorio.

UNIDAD 4

Las asignaturas y los horarios ▬▬▬▬▬▬▬▬ LECCIÓN 1

7 LAS ASIGNATURAS

★★ **Write** each school subject beside the sentence that best describes it.

~~Matemáticas~~	Estudios Sociales	Música	Dibujo
Educación Física	Informática	Filosofía	Química
Historia del Arte	Ciencias Naturales	Español	Inglés

En esta asignatura...

a. usamos la calculadora. ⟶ Matemáticas

b. aprendemos a tocar instrumentos y a cantar. ⟶ ....

c. hacemos deporte y gimnasia. ⟶ ....

d. usamos las computadoras. ⟶ ....

e. estudiamos obras de arte *(art work)* y sus autores. ⟶ ....

f. estudiamos la naturaleza y el medioambiente. ⟶ ....

g. usamos pinturas y somos creativos. ⟶ ....

h. estudiamos los territorios con mapas. ⟶ ....

i. estudiamos la cultura y el idioma hispanos. ⟶ ....

j. vamos al laboratorio y hacemos experimentos. ⟶ ....

k. estudiamos grandes pensadores y pensadoras *(thinkers)*. ⟶ ....

l. estudiamos la cultura y el idioma ingleses. ⟶ ....

8 LAS ASIGNATURAS

★★ **Fill in** the chart with two subjects you are studying this year.

ASIGNATURA	HORARIO	PROFESOR O PROFESORA
Ejemplo: Tecnología	Los martes a las once menos diez y los miércoles a las once y treinta y cinco.	Sra. Stephany Lambert

UNIDAD 4

Copyright © by Difusión, S. L.

Las asignaturas y los horarios

LECCIÓN 1

MI VOCABULARIO

9 LAS ASIGNATURAS • EL HORARIO ESCOLAR

★★ **A. Look at** Samuel's class schedule and **listen to** his voice message.
🔊 **Fill in** the blanks with the missing subjects.

	LUNES	MARTES	MIÉRCOLES	JUEVES	VIERNES
7:00 - 7:50	Español	Inglés	Ciencias Naturales	Historia del Arte	b. ....
7:50 - 8:40	Español	Matemáticas	Ciencias Naturales	Historia del Arte	Español
8:40 - 9:30	Física	Música	Español	Inglés	Estudios Sociales
9:30 - 9:50			a.		
9:50 - 10:40	Filosofía	Informática	Religión	Química	c. ....
10:40 - 11:30	Inglés	Ética	Informática	Matemáticas	Tecnología
11:30 - 12:20	Inglés	Educación Física	Educación Física	Matemáticas	d. ....
12:20 - 01:40			A L M U E R Z O		
01:40 - 02:30	Estudios Sociales	Filosofía	Dibujo	Estudios Sociales	e. ....

B. Look at Samuel's class schedule again.
Answer the questions in complete sentences.

a. ¿Qué días tiene Educación Física?

   Samuel tiene Educación Física los martes y los miércoles.

b. ¿Con qué asignatura empieza las clases los martes?

   ....

c. ¿Con qué asignatura termina las clases los martes?

   ....

d. ¿Qué asignatura tiene los jueves antes del almuerzo?

   ....

e. ¿Qué tiene Samuel cada día a las doce y veinte?

   ....

UNIDAD 4

Las asignaturas y los horarios LECCIÓN 1

MI GRAMÁTICA

10 **TELLING TIME**

★ **Match** the times (**a–f**) with the corresponding clocks (**1–6**).

a. Es la una.

b. Son las nueve y cuarto.

c. Son las diez menos veinticinco.

d. Son las tres y cuarto.

e. Son las once.

f. Son las siete y media.

1. 07:30

2. 01:00

3. 03:15

4. 09:15

5. 11:00

6. 09:35

11 **TELLING TIME • RECUERDA: ADVERBS OF FREQUENCY**

★★ **Look at** Juan José's class schedule in the Student Edition.
Answer the questions in complete sentences.

a. ¿A qué hora termina Español los jueves?

Los jueves termina Español a las...

....

b. ¿A qué hora tiene Filosofía los martes?

....

....

c. ¿A qué hora empieza Educación Física los miércoles?

....

....

12 **STEM-CHANGING VERBS: EMPEZAR** (E > IE)

★★ **Complete** the sentences with the correct form of **empezar**.

a. ● Este año ___empiezo___ el grado 8, ¿y ustedes?

o Nosotros .... el grado 9.

● Y tú, ¿qué grado ...., Mariana?

b. ● Evelyn, ¿a qué hora .... tus hermanos las clases?

o Carlos .... a las siete y Sofía .... a las ocho.

UNIDAD 4

Uniformes escolares

MI VOCABULARIO

13 **LA ROPA**
★ **Unscramble** these words.

A C I M S A

la camisa

S T E C A I A M

la ....

L A F A D

la ....

T A N L Ó A N P

el ....

T U R É S E

el ....

D U E D A S A R

la ....

14 **LA ROPA • LOS ACCESORIOS**
★★ **Look at** this girl's uniform.
Decide whether the sentences are true (**T**) or false (**F**).

a. La muchacha lleva una falda gris. ☒ F

b. Lleva un pantalón negro. T F

c. Lleva muchos accesorios. T F

d. Lleva unos zapatos negros. T F

e. Lleva unos tenis negros. T F

f. Lleva una camisa blanca. T F

g. Lleva un suéter gris. T F

h. Lleva una camiseta blanca. T F

i. Lleva unos aretes. T F

j. Lleva unas medias blancas. T F

UNIDAD 4

Uniformes escolares

MI VOCABULARIO

15 LA ROPA • LOS ACCESORIOS

★★ **A. Look** at the picture and **choose** two students.
Describe their uniforms (clothes and accessories).
Mention three clothing items they wear and one they don't wear.

El / La estudiante lleva...

....

....

....

El / La estudiante lleva...

....

....

....

B. In pairs, **swap** your descriptions.
Can you **guess** which students your partner has described?

UNIDAD 4

Uniformes escolares ▬▬▬▬▬▬▬▬▬▬▬▬▬▬▬▬ LECCIÓN 1

MI GRAMÁTICA

16 **STEM-CHANGING VERBS: PODER** (O > UE)

★ **Listen to** a Student's Handbook from a Colombian school.

🔊 **Underline** the correct negative or affirmative option.

a. Los estudiantes **no pueden / pueden** llevar accesorios, como por ejemplo aretes.

b. Los estudiantes **no pueden / pueden** llevar el uniforme incompleto y sucio.

c. Las muchachas **no pueden / pueden** usar un poco de maquillaje con el uniforme.

d. Los muchachos **no pueden / pueden** tener el pelo de colores, por ejemplo, azul.

17 **STEM-CHANGING VERBS: PODER** (O > UE)

★★ **Write** two complete sentences that describe things you are allowed to do at your school. **Write** two complete sentences that describe things you are not allowed to do.

....

....

....

....

....

18 **STEM-CHANGING VERBS: PODER** (O > UE)

★ **Fill** in the blanks with **o** or **ue**.

● ¿Ustedes p........den ir sin el uniforme al colegio?

○ Nosotros no p........demos. En mi colegio es obligatorio llevar uniforme.

● Yo sí p........do. Nosotros no tenemos uniforme.

19 **STEM-CHANGING VERBS: PODER** (O > UE)

★★ **Complete** the sentences with the correct form of **poder**.

a. En la biblioteca, ustedes .... estudiar.

b. Mi prima Alex .... usar maquillaje con el uniforme.

c. Los estudiantes del colegio La Salle no .... llevar accesorios.

d. En el patio, mis compañeros y yo .... jugar al baloncesto.

UNIDAD 4

Las normas del colegio

MI VOCABULARIO

20 EL PERMISO Y LA PROHIBICIÓN

★ **Look at** the pictures. What is allowed (in **green**) and forbidden (in **red**) at this school?
Complete the sentences with **está prohibido** or **está permitido**.

a  b  c  d

e  f  g  h

En este colegio...

e. .... llevar zapatos de colores.

f. .... llevar las medias por debajo de la rodilla.

g. .... comer chocolate.

h. .... subir a los árboles.

i. .... leer cómics en clase.

j. .... reír en clase.

k. .... comer caramelos.

l. .... mascar chicle.

UNIDAD 4

Las normas del colegio

MI VOCABULARIO

21 **EL PERMISO Y LA PROHIBICIÓN**

★★★ **Imagine** your ideal school.

Write seven complete sentences to describe the rules (**el reglamento**).

You can use the activities below or think about other ones.

Include at least two forbidden activities.

llevar uniforme   tocar la guitarra en los recreos   bailar en el patio   hablar en clase

usar el celular en clase   comer en el gimnasio   estudiar en el auditorio   ...

REGLAMENTO DEL COLEGIO

1. Está permitido comer caramelos en todas las partes del colegio.

2. ....

3. ....

4. ....

5. ....

6. ....

7. ....

UNIDAD 4

Las normas del colegio

MI GRAMÁTICA

22 **RECUERDA: TELLING TIME**

★ **Write** the times in words.

a. Son las tres y... ....

b. ....

c. ....

d. ....

23 **RECUERDA: STEM-CHANGING VERBS: EMPEZAR** (E > IE)

★ **Complete** the sentences with the correct form of the verbs in parentheses.

a. ● ¿Ustedes a qué hora **(empezar)** ....empiezan.... las clases?

○ Nosotros **(empezar)** .... las clases a las siete.

Y tú, ¿a qué hora **(empezar)** ....?

b. Mariana **(preferir)** .... tomar el almuerzo a las doce y media.

c. Los estudiantes no **(entender)** .... la actividad.

d. Profesora, ¿a qué hora **(empezar)** .... la clase de Español?

24 **RECUERDA: STEM-CHANGING VERBS: EMPEZAR (E > IE), PODER** (O > UE)

★★★ **Complete** this text with the following verbs below in the correct form.

 querer (x2)   poder (x2)   tener (x2)

FUNDACION
PIES
DESCALZOS

Shakira es una artista colombiana que ᵃ ....piensa.... en las personas necesitadas y ᵇ .... ayudar a su comunidad. Ella es la creadora de la Fundación Pies Descalzos. Gracias a Pies Descalzos, muchos jóvenes de comunidades pobres en Colombia ᶜ .... tener una educación de calidad. También hay muchos estudiantes que ᵈ .... ir a la universidad con sus becas *(scholarship)*.

La fundación de Shakira ᵉ .... tres colegios en Colombia. Todos los colegios ᶠ .... muchos salones de clase y espacios para actividades culturales y deportivas.

En el futuro, la artista ᵍ .... crear más colegios en otros países.

Comunicación

1 INTERPRETIVE READING

You are going to read an email from Pedro, a Colombian student.

De: Pedro Oliver

Para: Michaella Jaime

Cc Bcc

Asunto: Mi colegio nuevo

Hola, Michaella:

¡Tengo más información sobre mi cole nuevo 🏫 ! Ya tengo el horario 📅 de este año: empezamos las clases a las 07:00 🕖 de la mañana y terminamos a las 02:30 🕝 de la tarde. Tengo media hora de recreo, de 09:30 🕤 a 10:00 🕙 .

El mejor día es el viernes porque empezamos con Dibujo 🎨 y terminamos con Estudios Sociales 🌐 . También tenemos Educación Física ⛹ a las 12:00, en la cancha de deporte, y Química antes del recreo, en el laboratorio 🔬 . Me gusta mucho cambiar[1] de salón de clase, ¡así el día es más divertido!, ¿verdad? Ahora mi asignatura 📖 favorita es Inglés. Me gusta mucho mi profesora . Se llama Delphine, es muy simpática, ¡y sus clases son muuuy entretenidas!

En el cole nuevo también tenemos que llevar uniforme..., pero podemos llevar ropa de varios colores, ¡no solo de color blanco y negro! Por ejemplo, las camisetas 👕 , las sudaderas, las medias 🧦 y los tenis. ¡Ah! Pero está prohibido llevar accesorios... Y yo no puedo llevar mi arete, como hago normalmente 😣 .

Y tú, ¿qué clases tienes? ¿Hay alguna novedad[2] interesante en el colegio?

¡Hasta pronto!

Un saludo,

Pedro

↩ Responder   ➜ Reenviar

1 change   2 update

(Before reading)

A. Read the email's subject (**asunto**) and **look at** the emojis on the previous page. What do you think the email is about?

....

....

(First reading)

B. Read the email on the previous page.
Answer the questions in complete sentences.

1. ¿Cuándo empieza y termina las clases Pedro? *Write the times in words.*

Pedro empieza las clases a las...

....

2. ¿Cuál es el día favorito de Pedro? ....

3. ¿En qué asignaturas cambia de salón de clase? ....

....

....

4. ¿Qué accesorio lleva Pedro normalmente? ....

(Second reading)

C. Decide whether the sentences are true (**T**) or false (**F**).
Correct the false sentences.

1. El recreo de Pedro empieza a las diez y media y termina a las once. [T] [F]

....

2. La ropa del uniforme de Pedro es siempre de color blanco y negro. [T] [F]

....

3. En el colegio nuevo está permitido llevar accesorios. [T] [F]

....

4. La asignatura favorita de Pedro es Química. [T] [F]

....

UNIDAD 4

Comunicación

INTERPRETIVE

2 INTERPRETIVE LISTENING

Ms. Díaz teaches in a Colombian school. She spotted some mistakes in the class schedule. You are going to listen to Ms. Díaz explaining the changes to her students.

(Before listening)

A. Look at the class schedule and **read aloud** the times.
It will help you to better understand the audio.

	LUNES	MARTES	MIÉRCOLES	JUEVES	VIERNES
08:30 – 09:20	Español	Matemáticas	Música	Dibujo	Tecnología
09:25 – 10:15	Dibujo	Filosofía	Matemáticas	Inglés	Informática
RECREO					
10:35 – 11:25	Matemáticas	Español	Ciencias Naturales	Español	Inglés
11:30 – 12:20	Historia del Arte	Educación Física	Química	Español	Estudios Sociales
ALMUERZO					
12:40 – 01:30	Ciencias Naturales	Estudios Sociales	Historia del Arte	Ciencias Naturales	Música
01:35 – 02:25	Dibujo	Inglés	Educación Física	Ética	Educación Física

🔊 (First and second listen)

B. Listen to Ms. Díaz and **correct** the class schedule above.

C. Listen to the audio **again** and **check** that you have gotten the correct information.

UNIDAD 4

Comunicación

PRESENTATIONAL

3 PRESENTATIONAL WRITING

Fundación Pies Descalzos has just opened a new school in Barranquilla.
You are going to write an article about the new school for *Somos reporteros*.

Before writing

A. Write key words you are going to use in the article.

B. Consider **looking at** pictures of another Pies Descalzos school on the internet to get inspired.

C. Write in your notebook the activities students can do in each part of the school building.

Write the article

D. Follow the structure.

Write a title. ⎯⎯⎯⎯⎯

....

El colegio nuevo de Pies Descalzos se llama...

....

Write six complete sentences to describe the new school.

Include:
- nombre del colegio
- partes del colegio más importantes
- horarios
- uniformes
- funciones / usos
- ...

....
....
....
....
....
....
....
....
....
....
....

Share your opinion about the school.

Creo que el colegio es...
....
....
....

UNIDAD 4

Comunicación

PRESENTATIONAL

4 PRESENTATIONAL SPEAKING

Imagine that you are a vlogger.
You are going to create a video about a day at your school.

(Prepare the video)

A. Write a script in your notebook.

1. Decide what information you want to share:
your name, where you live, your school's name,
your school year, etc.

> Me llamo... y vivo en...
> El nombre de mi colegio es...

2. Explain what you normally do at school:

- What time do you start and finish shool?
- What time do you have a break and have lunch?
- What subjects do you have?
- In which parts of the building do you have the previous activities?

> Las clases empiezan a las...
> Los lunes tenemos...

3. Say goodbye to your followers.

(Practice and record yourself)

B. Practice several times.
Pay attention to your pronunciation—it will count toward your grade!
Repeat the words or sentences that are especially difficult for you.

C. Record your video.
Look at the camera to connect with your followers.
Make sure that you record in a quiet place
that is free from interruptions.

ESTRATEGIA

Watch your body language

Nonverbal language will help you increase clarity and will add interest to your video. Being more **aware of the importance of body language and nonverbal communication** will make you become a better vlogger.

Comunicación

INTERPERSONAL

5 INTERPERSONAL WRITING

You are going to reply to a social media post from an educational foundation.

(Read the post)

A. What does this foundation need help with?

....

....

....

....

....

Fundación Educación para Todos (Seguir) ∨

Queremos tu ayuda para diseñar el uniforme y su reglamento de uso para nuestra nueva escuela situada en Barranquilla (Colombia). ¿Nos ayudas con tu propuesta?
#EducacionParaTodos

12:00 AM - 3 jun 2021

21 Retweet **34** Me gusta

 ♡ 12   ⟲ 21   ♡ 34   ✉

(Write your answer)

B. Describe your proposal: clothing and accessories for the uniform.
Say when the clothing and accessories should be worn.
Try to be creative! For instance, students can wear a different uniform depending on the day.

Responder a Fundación Educación para Todos   (Responder)

Los estudiantes pueden llevar...

....

....

....

....

....

....

....

UNIDAD 4

¿Cómo estás?

MI VOCABULARIO

1 LOS ESTADOS DE ÁNIMO

★ **Find** ten adjectives hidden in the puzzle below.

A	F	E	L	I	Z	R	A	C	N	T	U
U	T	A	O	Y	V	E	E	O	U	R	Y
C	R	I	N	J	Y	L	H	N	D	A	B
A	I	V	S	K	A	A	O	T	A	N	I
N	S	N	S	T	D	J	A	E	F	Q	E
S	T	U	B	S	E	A	N	N	O	U	N
A	E	U	G	O	M	D	O	T	S	I	O
D	O	E	N	O	J	A	D	O	O	L	Q
O	T	R	O	I	E	S	T	A	Y	A	H
P	R	E	O	C	U	P	A	D	O	E	Ñ
M	A	L	E	F	G	X	Y	A	R	F	R

a. feliz

b. ....

c. ....

d. ....

e. ....

f. ....

g. ....

h. ....

i. ....

j. ....

2 LOS ESTADOS DE ÁNIMO

★★ **Place** the adjectives of the previous activity in the corresponding column.

UNIDAD 4

¿Cómo estás?

MI VOCABULARIO

3 LOS ESTADOS DE ÁNIMO

★★ **Look at** the illustration. How does each person feel?
Complete the sentences below to describe their feelings.

Primer día de colegio

Diferentes puntos de vista

¡¡Buaaaaaaá!!   ¡¡Yujuuuuu!!   Ughhh...   ¡¡Síííííííí!!

preescolar   **primaria**   **bachillerato**   **universidad**   **mamás y papás**

a. El niño de preescolar está... ....

b. La niña de primaria ....

c. El estudiante de bachillerato ....

d. La estudiante universitaria ....

e. Las mamás y los papás ....

4 LOS ESTADOS DE ÁNIMO • LA VIDA EN EL COLEGIO (1)

★★★ **Write** complete sentences to describe your feelings in each situation.
Note that some of the verbs you need to conjugate are irregular.

a. sacar una mala nota ⟶ Cuando saco una mala nota... ....

b. suspender un examen ⟶ ....

c. tener muchas tareas ⟶ ....

d. aprender algo nuevo ⟶ ....

e. tener descanso ⟶ ....

f. divertirse ⟶ ....

UNIDAD 4

¿Cómo estás?

LECCIÓN 2

MI GRAMÁTICA

5 **ESTAR** + FEELINGS AND MOODS

★ **Read** these sentences.
Place each highlighted adjective in a box next to the category in which it belongs.

a. Estoy un poco **preocupado** por el examen de mañana.

b. Aurora casi nunca está **enojada**; es una persona muy **simpática**.

c. Mi perro Tobby es muy **leal**.

d. Mis padres están **cansados** por sus trabajos.

e. Mi hermano es una persona muy **independiente**.

To describe feelings and moods	→	preocupado , _____ , _____ .

To describe personality	→	_____ , _____ , _____ .

6 **ESTAR** + FEELINGS AND MOODS

★★ **Combine** the words from the three columns to create sentences.

a.	Yo		están		muy simpáticas.
b.	Nicolás y tú		soy		muy enojada.
c.	Mariana y Eva		está		un poco tímido/a.
d.	Gabriela		son		un poco tristes.

7 **ESTAR** + FEELINGS AND MOODS

★★★ **Fill in** the blanks with the correct form of **ser** or **estar**.

a. Alejandro ___está___ nervioso. Mañana es su primer día de colegio.

b. ¿_____ contentos con su profesor?

c. Enrique _____ muy amable, pero hoy _____ de mal humor.

d. Cecilia y Marta _____ relajadas porque no tienen tareas.

e. ¿Dónde _____ vuestro colegio?

f. Mis compañeros y yo _____ preocupados por el examen de mañana.

UNIDAD 4

Copyright © by Difusión, S. L.

Los sistemas escolares ████████████████████ LECCIÓN 2

MI VOCABULARIO

8 **LA VIDA EN EL COLEGIO (2 Y 3)**

★ **Complete** the sentences with **fácil**, **difícil**, **temprano**, or **tarde**.

a. A Eva no le gustan los números, pero le gusta mucho la naturaleza.

Para Eva, la clase de Matemáticas es más .... que la de Ciencias Naturales.

b. Juan José quiere empezar las clases a las 8 de la mañana, y no a las 6:50.

Juan José prefiere empezar las clases más .... por las mañanas.

c. Arturo dibuja muy bien, pero no le gusta cantar.

Para Arturo, la clase de Dibujo es más .... que la clase de Música.

d. Laura prefiere comer a la 1:30, y no a las 2:30, como hace normalmente.

Laura prefiere comer más .... que ahora.

9 **LA VIDA EN EL COLEGIO (2)**

★★ In your opinion, what is the best way to learn a language?
Write four complete sentences.
Select one element from each column.

| ver series en español |
| escuchar música en español |
| usar siempre el traductor automático |
| hablar con personas hispanohablantes |
| no hacer las tareas de Español |
| leer novelas escritas en español |

+ es bueno / es malo + para aprender español

1. Ver series en español es... ....

2. ....

....

3. ....

....

4. ....

....

UNIDAD 4

Los sistemas escolares

MI GRAMÁTICA

10 COMPARATIVES

★ **Put** the puzzle pieces **together** and **write** complete sentences.

a Esperanza.
que tiene
Natalia
horas de clase
más

b empieza las clases
más que
Juan José
su amiga Guadalupe.
temprano

c que
estudian
los estadounidenses.
menos español
Los portugueses

a. Natalia tiene... ....

b. ....

c. ....

11 COMPARATIVES

★★ **Write** comparisons about the **reporteros** using **más / menos que**.

a. Guada tener (-) vacaciones Laura

→ Guada tiene menos vacaciones que Laura. ....

b. Juan José empezar las clases (+) temprano Laura → ....

....

c. Laura terminar las clases (+) tarde Juan José → ....

....

d. Laura tener (-) clases Juan José → ....

....

e. Juan José estudiar (+) Guada → ....

....

f. Juan José tener (-) tiempo libre Guada y Laura → ....

....

UNIDAD 4

Los sistemas escolares

LECCIÓN 2

● **MI GRAMÁTICA**

12 **COMPARATIVES**

★ **Look at** the infographic and **decide** whether the sentences below are true (**T**) or false (**F**).
Correct the false sentences.

¿Qué países estudian español?
Países con más estudiantes

Cantidad de estudiantes

30 000   4 000 000   8 000 000

Canadá · Suecia · Noruega · Polonia · China · Alemania · Reino Unido · Japón · Irlanda · Francia · EE. UU. · España · Portugal · Marruecos · Senegal · Italia · Filipinas · Camerún · Brasil · Benín · Guinea Ecuatorial · Costa de Marfil · Gabón

↑ *El español: una lengua viva. Informe 2020*, Instituto Cervantes

a. Los Estados Unidos tienen menos estudiantes de español que Canadá. ☐ T ☒

   Los Estados Unidos tienen... ....

b. En Francia hay más estudiantes de español que en China. ☐ T ☐ F

....

c. En Reino Unido hay más estudiantes de español que en Brasil. ☐ T ☐ F

....

d. Francia tiene menos estudiantes de español que Guinea Ecuatorial. ☐ T ☐ F

....

e. Japón tiene más estudiantes de español que los Estados Unidos. ☐ T ☐ F

....

UNIDAD 4

El Día del Maestro

LECCIÓN 2

MI VOCABULARIO

13 LA PERSONALIDAD Y LAS CUALIDADES (1)
★ **Read** the poster.
Underline the correct adjective in each sentence (a–d).

LOS MEJORES PROFESORES DEL MUNDO

Explican lo que no entendemos muchas veces.

Inventan cosas nuevas cada día.

Explican siempre cosas increíbles.

Ayudan a los estudiantes a tener interés.

a. Son los más **pacientes / impacientes** del mundo.

b. Son los más **innovadores / estrictos** del mundo.

c. Son los más **interesantes / tolerantes** del mundo.

d. Son los más **motivadores / aburridos** del mundo.

SUPERPROFESOR   **SUPERPROFESORA**

#FELIZ DÍA DEL MAESTRO

14 LA PERSONALIDAD Y LAS CUALIDADES (1) • LA VIDA EN EL COLEGIO (1, 2, 3 Y 4)
★★ **Think of** a **superprofesor** or a **superprofesora** from your school.
What qualities does he or she have? **Write** two complete sentences.

....

....

....

....

UNIDAD 4

El Día del Maestro LECCIÓN 2

● **MI VOCABULARIO**

15 **LA PERSONALIDAD Y LAS CUALIDADES (1)**
★ **Place** the adjectives in the corresponding box according to your opinion.

innovador/a   interesante   aburrido/a   divertido/a   negativo/a   impaciente

estricto/a   positivo/a   motivador/a   paciente   exigente   tolerante

👍 innovador/a

👎

●

16 **LA PERSONALIDAD Y LAS CUALIDADES (1)**
★★ Alberto and Alejandra are totally opposite people.
Fill in the blanks with the corresponding antonyms.
Note that you need to **make** the noun-adjective agreement.

Alberto es...		Alejandra es...
a. paciente		impaciente
b. aburrido	≠	
c.		estricta
d. negativo		
e.		tradicional

17 **LA VIDA EN EL COLEGIO (1, 2, 3 Y 4)**
★★★ **Write** a short thank-you note to recognize your teachers' work.
You can use: **dar las gracias**, **amar**, **enseñar**, **aprender**, and **reconocer su trabajo**.

● ....

....

....

UNIDAD 4

El Día del Maestro

LECCIÓN 2

MI GRAMÁTICA

18 **SUPERLATIVES (1)**

★ **Complete** the sentences about this group of friends.

	Roberta	Mariana	Gabriela
alta	1.62 m	1.60 m	1.68 m
positiva	++	+++	++
divertida	+++	++	+
paciente	++	+	+++

a. Gabriela **(alta)** es la muchacha más alta del grupo.

b. Mariana **(positiva)** ....

c. Roberta **(divertida)** ....

d. Mariana **(paciente)** ....

e. Gabriela **(divertida)** ....

19 **SUPERLATIVES (1)**

★★ **Write** three complete sentences about your classes, using the adjectives below.
Use the superlative form.

fácil   difícil   ~~divertido/a~~   aburrido/a   divertido/a   motivador/a

a. Para mí, la asignatura más divertida del curso es....

b. ....

c. ....

20 **SUPERLATIVES (1) • RECUERDA: COMPARATIVES**

★★★ **Fill in** the blanks with **que** or **de**.

a. El horario de Daniela es mejor ....que.... el horario de Joseph.

b. Tú eres el estudiante más trabajador .... toda la clase.

c. Los lunes termino el colegio más tarde .... los viernes.

d. El señor Smith es el profesor más exigente .... nuestro colegio.

e. La clase de Inglés es más divertida .... la clase de Dibujo.

Quiero ser personero/a

MI VOCABULARIO

21 **RECUERDA: LA PERSONALIDAD Y LAS CUALIDADES (1)**
★ **Match** the words (**a–f**) with the corresponding antonyms (**1–6**).

a. tranquilo/a

b. tímido/a

c. cariñoso/a

d. trabajador/a

e. divertido/a

f. dependiente

1. independiente

2. perezoso/a

3. aburrido/a

4. abierto/a

5. nervioso/a

6. distante

22 **LA PERSONALIDAD Y LAS CUALIDADES (1 Y 2)**
★★ **Fill in** the blanks with the correct adjectives.

creativa responsable tímida positiva fiable trabajadora

a. Michael estudia mucho. Es una persona muy ___trabajadora___.

b. Emmanuel tiene mucha imaginación.
Es una persona muy _____.

c. Sara cree que todos los problemas tienen solución.
Es una persona _____.

d. Evelyn es una candidata que siempre hace lo que promete.
Es una persona _____.

e. Yo no soy una persona abierta, en general.
Soy una persona un poco _____.

f. Nuestra personera siempre hace lo que tiene que hacer.
Es una persona _____.

23 **LA PERSONALIDAD Y LAS CUALIDADES (1 Y 2)**
★★★ What qualities do you think a **personero** or **personera** has to have? Why?
Write two complete sentences.

Un/a personero/a tiene que ser... .... porque... ....
....
Un/a personero/a no puede ser... .... porque... ....
....

UNIDAD 4

Quiero ser personero/a

MI VOCABULARIO

24 LAS ELECCIONES

★ **Match** the verbs (**a–d**) with the words (**1–4**).

a. votar

b. proponer

c. representar

d. hacer

1. una propuesta

2. una solución

3. por un/a candidato/a

4. a los / las compañeros/as

25 LAS ELECCIONES

★ **Find** the odd one out in each series.

a. la campaña electoral | las elecciones | el problema | el / la candidato/a

b. el / la candidato/a | el / la profesor/a | el / la representante | el / la personero/a

c. ser fiable | ser honesto/a | ser perezoso/a | ser responsable

d. votar | participar | representar | jugar

26 LAS ELECCIONES

★★ **Look at** the code (**código**) and **write** the words below.
Who does these activities: the **personero/a** or the other students? ....

código: 4 = A • 3 = E • 1 = i • 5 = O • 2 = U

a. H 4 C 3 R   P R 5 P 2 3 S T 4 S   R 3 4 L 1 S T 4 S

....

b. P 4 R T 1 C 1 P 4 R   3 N   2 N 4

C 4 M P 4 Ñ 4   3 L 3 C T 5 R 4 L

....

c. M 3 J 5 R 4 R   3 L   C 5 L 3 G 1 5

....

d. H 4 C 3 R   4 C T 1 V 1 D 4 D 3 S   P 4 R 4

T 5 D 5 S   L 4 S   C 5 M P 4 Ñ 3 R 5 S

....

UNIDAD 4

Copyright © by Difusión, S. L.

Quiero ser personero/a

MI GRAMÁTICA

27 SUPERLATIVES (2): MEJOR / PEOR

★★ **Fill in** the blank with **el mejor**, **la mejor**, **el peor**, or **la peor**.

a. Para hacer la tarea, ___el mejor___ lugar de la casa es el despacho. ¡Es muy grande!

b. La señora Núñez es _____ profesora del colegio: es motivadora y divertida.

c. _____ cualidad para un/a personero/a es ser perezoso/a.

d. Para jugar al baloncesto, _____ lugar del colegio es la cancha de deportes.

e. Para mí _____ estación del año es el invierno. No me gusta el frío.

28 SUPERLATIVES (2): MEJOR / PEOR

★★★ **Underline** the correct option in each sentence.

a. El lunes es el **malo** / **peor** día de la semana.

b. Nicolás es un **buen** / **mejor** candidato para ser personero.

c. Mariana es la **peor** / **mala** candidata para personera del colegio.

d. En mi colegio tenemos los **buenos** / **mejores** salones de clase del mundo.

e. Tengo los **mejores** / **malos** papás del mundo.

29 SUPERLATIVES (2): MEJOR / PEOR

★★ **Read** the statements of three students running for **personero** or **personera**. Who is the best candidate? And the worst? **Explain** why.

🔊 **Juliana** — Tenemos que respetar y aceptar a todas las personas. Mi propuesta es hacer actividades para eliminar el *bullying* y ser más amables.

Alejandro — Yo represento a todos los estudiantes porque todos somos importantes. Mi propuesta es organizar más eventos en el colegio.

Cecilia — Yo solo represento a los deportistas. Mi propuesta es construir siete canchas nuevas y dos piscinas gigantes en el patio.

El / La mejor candidato/a del colegio es... _____ porque...

....

....

....

UNIDAD 4

Comunicación

INTERPRETIVE

1 INTERPRETIVE READING

You are going to read an article from an educational magazine.

¡GRACIAS, PROFESORES Y PROFESORAS!

El día 5 de octubre celebramos el Día Mundial de los Docentes (*World Teachers' Day*). Es el día que propone la Unesco[1]
5 para dar las gracias y reconocer el trabajo de los profesores y las profesoras de todo el mundo.

Pero muchos países celebran
10 este día en otra fecha en honor a una personalidad de la educación importante de su país. Por ejemplo, en Colombia, el Día del Maestro es el 15 de
15 mayo, en honor a San Juan Bautista de La Salle.

COLOMBIA

En Colombia, el día 15 de mayo, el Ministerio de Educación da una distinción a los
20 mejores profesores del año del país. En los colegios, para celebrar el Día del Maestro, los estudiantes organizan un homenaje a todos los profesores y destacan sus cualidades: por ejemplo, ser pacientes, motivadores,
25 tolerantes, positivos, innovadores...

LA DISTINCIÓN

Este año el ganador de la distinción es Lewis Yansey Cañas Jaimes, un profesor de Inglés. Él es muy innovador y usa la tecnología en
30 todas sus clases. Además, es muy exigente y motivador: con él, los estudiantes aprenden muchas palabras y expresiones interesantes.

1 United Nations Educational, Scientific, and Cultural Organization

UNIDAD 4

LECCIÓN 2

(Before reading)

A. Look at the picture and **read** the title of the article.
Do you have a similar celebration in your country?
Do you think it is important to have a special day for the appreciation of teachers?

....

....

....

(First reading)

B. Decide whether the sentences below are true (**T**) or false (**F**).
Correct the false sentences.

El Día del Maestro...

1. es el 5 de octubre y lo celebran en todos los países del mundo. [T] [F]

....

2. los estudiantes reconocen el trabajo de todos sus profesores y profesoras. [T] [F]

....

3. el Gobierno de Colombia da una distinción a los mejores profesores del mundo. [T] [F]

....

4. los colegios colombianos hacen actividades conmemorativas especiales. [T] [F]

....

UNIDAD 4

(Second reading)

C. Answer the questions below.

1. Según el artículo, ¿qué cualidades tiene un buen profesor o una buena profesora?

....

....

2. ¿Cuáles son las cualidades del profesor colombiano ganador?

....

Comunicación

LECCIÓN 2

INTERPRETIVE

2 INTERPRETIVE LISTENING

A Colombian school is running an election for a new **personero** or **personera**. You are going to listen to a message from the principal about the election.

(Before listening)

A. Do you remember what a **personero** or **personera** is?

....

....

B. Write all the words you remember related to the topic **elecciones**.

....

....

....

🔊 (First listen)

C. Answer the questions.

1. ¿Qué tienen que hacer los candidatos? ....

....

....

2. ¿Qué tienen que hacer los estudiantes? ....

....

....

3. ¿Qué día son las elecciones? ....

🔊 (Second listen)

D. Complete the sentence according to the information you hear.

Un/a buen/a candidato/a tiene que ser...

....

....

UNIDAD 4

Comunicación

PRESENTATIONAL

3 PRESENTATIONAL WRITING

Imagine that you want to run for **personero** or **personera** in your school.
You are going to write a short statement about yourself for the school website.

(Write your statement)

A. Follow the structure below.

Introduce yourself:

• What is your name?

• What grade are you in?

Write complete sentences:

• Describe your qualities. Use four adjectives.

• Explain your motivations: Why do you want to be a **personero/a**?

• Describe three of your proposals: What's important to you? Who do you want to help?

UNIDAD 4

(After writing)

B. Proofread before submitting your writing.
   Correct any mistakes you may find.

   • Have you used the vocabulary from this unit? [Yes] [No]

   • Have you used **ser** and **estar** correctly? [Yes] [No]

   • Have you used the superlative form? [Yes] [No]

Comunicación ███████████████████████████ LECCIÓN 2

PRESENTATIONAL

4 **PRESENTATIONAL SPEAKING**

You are the **personero** or **personera** at your school and today is the first day of class.
You are going to record a message to welcome the new students.
You can record a video or a voice message.

(Prepare the video or the voice message)

A. Write the script in your notebook.

1. Introduce yourself (name and grade)
and **welcome** the new students to the school.

> Me llamo...
> ¡Bienvenidos y bienvenidas a...

2. Imagine how they might be feeling.

> Imagino que ustedes están...

3. Give them some advice about the school life.

> Un consejo: (no) tienen que... / (no) pueden...

4. Say goodbye and **thank** them for their attention.

(Practice and record yourself)

B. Practice several times.
Pay attention to your pronounciation—it will count toward your grade!
Repeat the words or sentences that are especially difficult for you.

C. Record yourself.
Make sure that you record in a quiet place
that is free from interruptions.

UNIDAD 4

Comunicación

INTERPERSONAL

5 INTERPERSONAL WRITING

You are going to reply to Juan José's post on a students' forum.

(Read the post)

A. Highlight the following information: what time he starts and finishes school, number of classes per day and length of each class, when the school year starts and finishes, and duration of holidays.

¿CÓMO FUNCIONA TU COLEGIO?

Juan José
Colombia

EL HORARIO ESCOLAR
Yo empiezo las clases muy temprano, a las siete, pero también termino temprano, a las dos de la tarde. Tengo ocho clases por día. En mi colegio, las clases son de 45 minutos y tenemos un descanso.

LAS VACACIONES
El curso escolar empieza en enero y termina en diciembre. Tenemos doce semanas de vacaciones en total 😊. ¿Cómo son sus colegios?

12 respuestas:

Laura
España

Yo empiezo y termino las clases más tarde que tú (de 8:00 a 2:30). Tengo seis clases por día, dos clases menos que tú, pero mis clases son 15 minutos más largas... En las vacaciones, coincidimos: ¡tengo tantas vacaciones como tú! El curso es de septiembre a junio. 😍

ver más comentarios ▼

UNIDAD 4

(Write your comment)

B. Explain what the schedule and holidays are like in your school.
Compare the information with Juan José's.
Use comparative and superlative forms.

CULTURE QUIZ

1 **¿Dónde está Colombia?**

a. En América del Norte. ☐

b. En Centroamérica. ☐

c. En América del Sur. ☐

2 **La capital de Colombia es...**

a. Barranquilla. ☐

b. Medellín. ☐

c. Bogotá. ☐

3 **¿Cuál de estas ciudades no está en Colombia?**

a. Cali. ☐

b. Cartagena de Indias. ☐

c. Caracas. ☐

d. Bogotá. ☐

4 **El objetivo de la fundación de la cantante colombiana Shakira es...**

a. ayudar a dar educación de calidad a todos los niños de Colombia. ☐

b. dar lecciones de música a los niños de colegios privados. ☐

c. crear academias para aprender español en Haití y Sudáfrica. ☐

5 **"El nombre de Colombia deriva del explorador Cristobal Colón".**

a. Verdadero. ☐

b. Falso. ☐

6 **"Colombia produce un café excepcional".**

a. Verdadero. ☐

b. Falso. ☐

7 **Un/a personero/a es un/a...**

a. representante de todos los estudiantes. ☐

b. representante de los estudiantes del último grado. ☐

c. profesor/a del colegio. ☐

8 **¿Cuántos habitantes tiene Colombia?**

a. 10 millones. ☐

b. 50 millones. ☐

c. 100 millones. ☐

9 **¿Cuándo es el Día del Maestro en Colombia?**

a. El 15 de febrero. ☐

b. El 15 de mayo. ☐

c. El 15 de octubre. ☐

d. El 15 de noviembre. ☐

FELIZ DÍA DEL MAESTRO

10 **¿Qué no debe hacer un/a personero/a?**

a. Tener muchas propuestas. ☐

b. Mejorar el colegio. ☐

c. Pensar solo en sus amigos/as. ☐

d. Escuchar a sus compañeros/as. ☐

UNIDAD 4

5 Una semana conmigo

1 **Watch** the video.
Answer the questions.

1. ¿Qué idiomas habla Laura en su casa?

....
....

2. ¿Qué tres estereotipos sobre España aparecen en el video?

....
....

3. ¿Cómo es la gente de Madrid según *(according to)* Laura?

....
....

4. ¿Dónde está la Sagrada Familia? ¿Quién es su arquitecto?

....
....

5. ¿Qué museo menciona Laura? ¿Dónde está?

....
....

NAME .... CLASS .... DATE ....

Por la mañana

LECCIÓN 1

MI VOCABULARIO

2 **LA RUTINA • LOS CONECTORES**

★★★ **Listen to** Claudia's inteview about her routine.

🔊 **Put a mark** (✓) in the box of the correct answer and **write** the action.

a. ¿Qué hace Claudia primero?

1 ✓

Se levanta

2

3

b. ¿Qué hace antes de vestirse y peinarse?

1

2

3

c. ¿Qué hace después de desayunar?

1

2

3

d. ¿Qué hace finalmente?

1

2

3

UNIDAD 5

Copyright © by Difusión, S. L.

Por la mañana

MI VOCABULARIO

3 LA RUTINA

★ **Match** the sentences (**a–h**) with the correct numbers (**1–8**) from the illustration.

a. Hugo se levanta. ☐ 4

b. Esteban se peina. ☐

c. Lucía se lava la cara. ☐

d. Liliana se cepilla los dientes. ☐

e. Felipe hace la cama. ☐

f. Tere prepara el desayuno. ☐

g. Marta pasea al perro. ☐

h. Clara desayuna. ☐

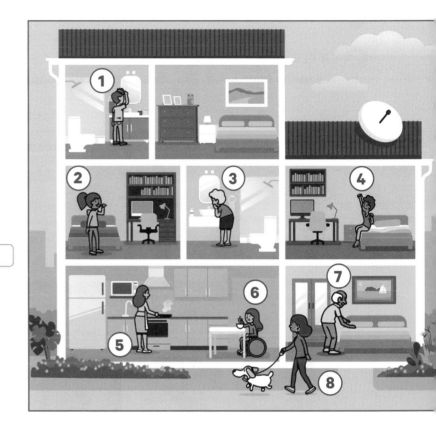

4 EL DESAYUNO

★★ **Write** the names of these foods.

a. los cereales ....

b. ....

c. ....

d. ....

e. ....

f. ....

g. ....

h. ....

i. ....

j. ....

k. ....

l. ....

UNIDAD 5

Por la mañana

MI GRAMÁTICA

5 **REFLEXIVE VERBS:** **LAVARSE**

★ **Fill in** the blanks with the correct reflexive pronouns.

yo	**a** ___me___ levanto	nosotros/as	**d** _____ levantamos
tú	**b** _____ levantas	vosotros/as	**e** _____ levantáis
él / ella, usted	**c** _____ levanta	ellos / ellas, ustedes	**f** _____ levantan

6 **REFLEXIVE VERBS:** **LAVARSE** • **STEM-CHANGING VERBS:** **VESTIRSE** (E > I)

★ **Complete** the sentences with Ana's and Víctor's routine in the correct order.

(lavarse la cara) (ducharse) (vestirse) (cepillarse los dientes) (peinarse) (~~levantarse~~)

ANA: Primero, _se levanta_ ,

después, _____

_____

y, finalmente, _____ .

VÍCTOR: Primero, _____ ,

después, _____

_____

y, finalmente, _____ .

7 **REFLEXIVE VERBS:** **LAVARSE** • **STEM-CHANGING VERBS:** **VESTIRSE** (E > I)

★★★ **Complete** the sentences with the correct form of the verbs in parentheses.

a. Yo **(levantarse)** ___me levanto___ a las 7:30.

Y ustedes, ¿a qué hora **(levantarse)** _____ ?

b. Mis papás y yo siempre **(vestirse)** _____ después de desayunar.

c. Mis hermanos **(ducharse)** _____ antes de ir al colegio.

d. ¿Tú **(peinarse)** _____ todos los días?

e. Yo **(cepillarse)** _____ los dientes tres veces (*times*) por día.

f. Manuel **(lavarse)** _____ la cara por la mañana y antes de acostarse.

UNIDAD 5

Mi rutina diaria

LECCIÓN 1

MI VOCABULARIO

8 **LA RUTINA • LAS COMIDAS • LAS PARTES DEL DÍA**

★★ **Write** each verb in the spaces next to the part of day to which it corresponds.

cenar   levantarse   desayunar   hacer la tarea

acostarse   merendar   ~~despertarse~~   dormir

POR LA MAÑANA

a. despertarse, ...

....

....

POR LA TARDE

b. ....

....

....

POR LA NOCHE

c. ....

....

....

9 **LA RUTINA • LAS COMIDAS**

★★ **Read** the text *El sueño de la vida* in the Student Edition.
Put the actions below **in order** according to the text.

a. desayunar ☐

b. regresar a casa ☐

c. acostarse ☐

d. merendar ☐

e. llegar al colegio ☐

f. preparar la mochila ☐

g. cenar ☐

h. despertarse [1]

i. ducharse y vestirse ☐

j. almorzar ☐

UNIDAD 5

Mi rutina diaria

MI VOCABULARIO

⑩ LA RUTINA • LAS COMIDAS • LAS PARTES DEL DÍA

★★★ **Read** the text and **put** the illustrations **in order**.

🔊 Manu mira el móvil todo el tiempo: cuando se levanta, cuando desayuna, cuando toma el bus, antes de entrar en el instituto, en el recreo, en las clases... Sí, también en las clases cuando no lo ven los profesores.

Por la tarde, cuando llega a casa, va directo a su habitación. Todo está
5 desordenado, como siempre. "¿Por qué mi hermano Jaime nunca ordena sus cosas?" —piensa Manu. Y Manu tiene que ordenarlo todo él solo.

Luego, va a merendar. En la cocina está Cristina (su hermana) con Olga.

—¿Qué tal, Manu?

—Bien, ¿y tú?

10 —Aquí estudiando con tu hermana.

—¿Duermes en nuestra casa esta noche? —le pregunta Manu.
Y piensa: "Sí, por favor, sííí".

—Sí —le dice Olga.

Manu está muy contento: "Otra noche con Olga en la habitación de al lado. ¡Bien!".
15 Y dice, sin pensar:

—Guay.

Y, enseguida, se pone muy muy rojo[1]. Y piensa: "Ahora Olga sabe que me gusta. ¡Qué vergüenza![2]".

1 he blushes   2 How embarrassing!   ↑ Lourdes Miquel, *Las cosas del amor* (2014)

UNIDAD 5

 a 1

 b

 c

 d

 e

 f

 g

 h

Mi rutina diaria

LECCIÓN 1

● **MI GRAMÁTICA**

11 **THE VERB IR** • **RECUERDA: ADVERBS OF FREQUENCY**

★★ **Write** complete sentences to say how often you and your friends do these actions.
Use these words: **todos los días, a menudo, a veces, (casi) nunca**.

a. [yo] [ir al colegio] → Yo voy al colegio...

b. [mis amigos y yo] [ir a la piscina] → ....

....

c. [mi mejor amigo/a] [ir a la biblioteca] → ....

....

d. [yo] [ir a jugar al béisbol] → ....

....

12 **RECUERDA: STEM-CHANGING VERBS AND REFLEXIVE VERBS**

★ **Color** the stem-change in the verbs below. Careful, not all verb forms change.

	MERENDAR	ACOSTARSE	VESTIRSE
yo	meriendo	me acuesto	me visto
tú	meriendas	te acuestas	te vistes
él / ella, usted	merienda	se acuesta	se viste
nosotros/as	merendamos	nos acostamos	nos vestimos
vosotros/as	merendáis	os acostáis	os vestís
ellos / ellas, ustedes	meriendan	se acuestan	se visten

13 **RECUERDA: STEM-CHANGING VERBS, REFLEXIVE VERBS, AND TELLING TIME**

★★★ **Write** complete sentences to say at what time you do these actions.

a. [dormir (yo)] → Duermo de...   a...

b. [despertarse (yo)] → ....

c. [empezar el colegio (nosotros)] → ....

d. [almorzar (nosotros)] → ....

e. [merendar (yo)] → ....

f. [acostarse (yo)] → ....

UNIDAD 5

Después del colegio

MI VOCABULARIO

14 LAS ACTIVIDADES EXTRAESCOLARES

★ **Underline** the correct verb for each picture.

tocar / <u>jugar</u> / hacer al ajedrez

tocar / jugar / hacer la batería

tocar / jugar / hacer natación

tocar / jugar / hacer teatro

tocar / jugar / hacer al baloncesto

tocar / jugar / hacer la guitarra

tocar / jugar / hacer el piano

tocar / jugar / hacer al fútbol

UNIDAD 5

Después del colegio

MI VOCABULARIO

15 **LAS ACTIVIDADES EXTRAESCOLARES**

★★ **A. Listen to** this dialogue between three friends.

🔊 Who does what?

For each activity, **put a mark** (✓) in the column under the correct person.

	María	Raúl	Bea
a. taekwondo	✓		
b. teatro			
c. fútbol			
d. guitarra			
e. batería			
f. natación			

B. Write complete sentences to say what activities each person does.

1. María → María hace taekwondo y...

2. Raúl → ....

3. Bea → ....

16 **LAS ACTIVIDADES EXTRAESCOLARES**

★★ What extracurricular activities do you have? How often do you do them?

Write at least four complete sentences.

Ejemplo: Yo juego al baloncesto los martes y los jueves.

....

....

....

....

....

UNIDAD 5

Después del colegio

LECCIÓN 1

MI GRAMÁTICA

17 **RECUERDA: STEM-CHANGING VERBS:** **JUGAR** (U > UE)

★ **Conjugate jugar** in the present tense.

yo	^aj ue go		nosotros/as	^dj................gamos
tú	^bj................gas		vosotros/as	^ej................gáis
él / ella, usted	^cj................ga		ellos / ellas, ustedes	^fj................gan

18 **RECUERDA: STEM-CHANGING VERBS:** **ACOSTARSE** (O > UE) / **JUGAR** (U > UE)

★★ **Choose** the appropriate verb for each sentence and **conjugate** it to the correct form.

acostarse   aprobar   jugar   dormir   ~~poder~~

a. Hoy no ......puedo...... ir a clase de natación. Tengo mucha tarea del colegio.

b. Lola y Marc .... al tenis todos los sábados.

c. Y tú, ¿normalmente a qué hora .... por la noche?

d. Juliana siempre .... todos los exámenes. Es muy buena estudiante.

e. Hoy mi hermano .... en casa de un amigo.

19 **RECUERDA: REFLEXIVE VERBS, STEM-CHANGING VERBS, THE VERBS** **IR** **AND** **HACER**

★★ **Complete** the text with the following verbs in the correct form.

levantarse   acostarse   jugar (x2)   hacer (x3)   ir (x2)

Mis hermanos y yo ^a hacemos muchas actividades extraescolares.

Yo ^b .... todos los días a las seis de la mañana

porque ^c .... natación antes de ir al colegio.

Por las tardes, a veces ^d .... a clases de piano

y otras veces ^e .... al baloncesto.

Mi hermano Miguel ^f .... tarde los fines de semana

porque ^g .... al ajedrez en un grupo del barrio.

Mi hermana Inés ^h .... teatro con sus amigos del colegio.

A veces, mis papás y yo ⁱ .... a ver sus obras de teatro,

¡son muy divertidas!

UNIDAD 5

Copyright © by Difusión, S. L.

Deportes populares

LECCIÓN 1

MI VOCABULARIO

20 **LOS DEPORTES**

★ **Look at** the pictures.
Combine the words from the three colums to make sentences.

a. Marc Márquez   tenis

b. Garbiñe Muguruza   ciclismo

c. Sofía Mulanovich   hace   taekwondo

d. María del Rosario Espinoza   juega al   motociclismo

e. Egan Bernal   voleibol

f. Karla Ortiz   surf

UNIDAD 5

Copyright © by Difusión, S. L.

Deportes populares

MI VOCABULARIO

21 LOS DEPORTES
★★ **Complete** the crossword puzzle.

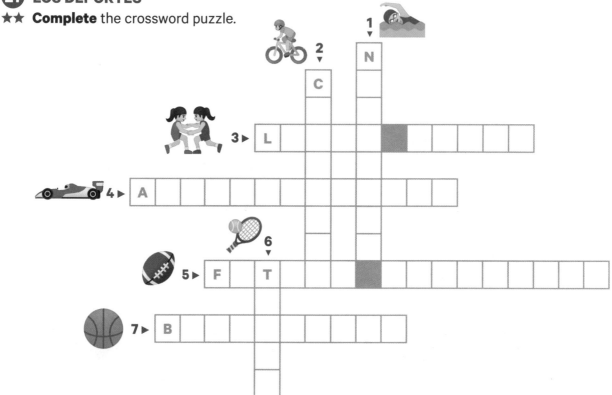

22 LOS DEPORTES
★★★ **Put a mark** (✓) in the correct answer.

a. Para jugar, tienes que usar un balón.

ciclismo ☐   fútbol ☐   natación ☐   automovilismo ☐

b. Para practicar este deporte, tienes que ir a una piscina.

natación ☐   tenis ☐   ciclismo ☐   hockey ☐

c. En este deporte, juegan dos equipos (teams) de cinco jugadores.

boxeo ☐   golf ☐   baloncesto ☐   tenis ☐

d. Para jugar, necesitas (you need) una mesa.

motociclismo ☐   ajedrez ☐   lucha libre ☐   taekwondo ☐

e. Es un deporte individual.

baloncesto ☐   fútbol ☐   surf ☐   béisbol ☐

UNIDAD 5

Deportes populares

MI VOCABULARIO

23 **LOS DEPORTES**

★★★ **Listen to** three friends from Argentina, Colombia, and Spain talk about athletes.

🔊 **Answer** the questions below.

YULIMAR ROJAS

LEO MESSI

MARC GASOL

CATERINE IBARGÜEN

a. ¿De qué país es Leo Messi?

Leo Messi es de...

b. ¿Qué deportes son populares en Argentina?

....

c. Nombra dos deportes muy populares en Colombia.

....

d. ¿Qué deporte hacen Caterine Ibargüen y Yulimar Rojas?

....

e. ¿Cuáles son los deportes más populares en España?

....

f. ¿Qué deporte practican los hermanos Gasol?

....

g. ¿Cuál es el deporte más popular en Argentina, Colombia y España?

....

UNIDAD 5

Comunicación

INTERPRETIVE

1 **INTERPRETIVE READING**

You are going to read an article about extracurricular activities in Spain.

🔊 ¿MUCHAS ACTIVIDADES EXTRAESCOLARES?

El 90% de los niños españoles hacen actividades extraescolares deportivas, educativas o artísticas. Las actividades más populares son
5 las actividades deportivas. Aprender idiomas es la segunda (2.ª) actividad más popular. Finalmente, están las actividades artísticas, como la música y la danza.

10 **"Días de trabajo muy largos"**

Muchos niños españoles se levantan muy temprano, están en el colegio todo el día y, después, van a una o a dos actividades extraescolares.
15 Cuando llegan a casa, es la hora de cenar, y después de cenar, tienen que hacer la tarea. Tienen días de trabajo muy largos, ¡más que los días de trabajo de sus papás!

20 Las actividades extraescolares ayudan a completar la educación de los niños y a tener un estilo de vida saludable. Pero los psicólogos piensan que los niños pueden sufrir estrés cuando
25 hacen demasiadas[1] actividades.

"Los niños necesitan aburrirse para ser más creativos"

Un número cada vez más grande de expertos opinan que los niños
30 necesitan tener tiempo para jugar para poder tener una mejor salud física y emocional. Además, los niños también necesitan aburrirse para ser más creativos. ¿Por qué? Porque
35 cuando un niño se aburre, inventa juegos, crea historias, construye objetos... y estas actividades estimulan su imaginación.

1 too much

UNIDAD 5

(Read the first paragraph (lines 1 – 9))

A. ¿Qué actividades extraescolares prefieren los estudiantes españoles de primaria? **Write** them in order of preference.

....

....

(Read the full text)

B. Correct the sentences below in order to make them true.

1. En España, cuando los estudiantes terminan las clases, van a sus casas y hacen la tarea.

En España, cuando los estudiantes terminan las clases, hacen una o dos actividades

extraescolares.

2. Las actividades extraescolares tienen un solo beneficio: completar la educación.

....

....

3. Según los expertos, los niños con muchas actividades extraescolares no sufren estrés.

....

....

4. Para ser más creativos, los niños tienen que hacer muchas actividades extraescolares.

....

....

(After reading)

C. Write complete sentences to answer the following questions.
¿Haces muchas actividades extraescolares?
¿Crees que tienes que hacer más o menos? ¿Por qué?

....

....

....

....

UNIDAD 5

Comunicación

INTERPRETIVE

2 **INTERPRETIVE LISTENING**

You are going to listen to a conversation between Alba and her friend.

(Before listening)

A. Read the questions from activity 2B.

Are there any difficult words for you?

Try to guess their meanings using context or cognates.

 (First listen)

B. Put a mark (✓) in the correct answer.

1. ¿Por qué está cansada Alba?

    a. Porque siempre tiene muchas tareas del colegio. ☐

    b. Porque tiene que entrenar para una competencia. ☐

    c. Porque tiene muchas actividades extraescolares. ☐

2. ¿Tiene que ir a la piscina los fines de semana?

    a. Sí, tiene que ir a la piscina los sábados y los domingos. ☐

    b. Solo va a la piscina los sábados. ☐

    c. Solo va a la piscina los domingos. ☐

 (Second listen)

C. Complete Alba's Saturday schedule.

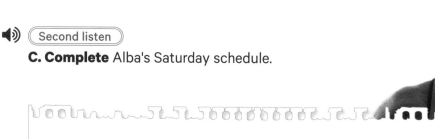

8:00	**a.** Se levanta y...
8:30	**b.**
9:00 - 01:30	**c.**
02:00	**d.** ... y duerme la siesta.
03:30 - 05:00	**e.**
06:00 - 08:00	**f.** Tiene tiempo libre, pero...
08:30	**g.** Cena y...
10:30	**h.**

UNIDAD 5

Comunicación

PRESENTATIONAL

3 **PRESENTATIONAL WRITING**

You are going to write an article about a sports personality for *Somos reporteros*.

(Before writing)

A. Write down information about the person: name, age, sport, etc.
This can be a real sports personality or a made-up one.

B. Make a list in your notebook about his / her daily routine.
You can make up the information.

6:30 - se despierta

...

(Write the article)

C. Follow the structure.

Write a title. ———

> **Un día en la vida de...** ....

Introduce the person,
using complete sentences:

- ¿Qué deporte practica?
- ¿Cuál es su logro
(*achievement*) **más**
importante?

> ....
>
> Es campeón / campeona de... ....
>
> ....
>
> ....

> Se levanta a las... ....

Describe their routine,
using complete sentences:

- ¿A qué hora se levanta?
- ¿A qué hora entrena
(*trains*)?
- ¿A qué hora almuerza?
- etc.

Use linking words:
**primero, luego, después,
finalmente, antes de,
después de...**

UNIDAD 5

Comunicación

PRESENTATIONAL

4 **PRESENTATIONAL SPEAKING**

A radio program has asked its audience to send voice messages describing:
Mi día más loco (crazy) *de la semana.*
You are going to record a voice message for the program.

(Prepare the voice message)

A. Underline the most stressful day of the week for you.

Mi día más loco es el **lunes / martes / miércoles / jueves / viernes / sábado / domingo**.

B. Write the script in your notebook.

1. Describe your routine that day.

> Primero, me levanto a las 6:15 h de la mañana. Después…

2. Explain what extracurricular activities you do that day.
Mention the hours or the parts of the day when you do these activities.
You can make up information in order to make this day even crazier!

> A las… hago… / voy a…

ESTRATEGIA

Linking words

Linking words will make your speech more logical and fluent while helping you **boost your Spanish.**

3. Use linking words to connect your ideas:
primero, luego, después, finalmente, antes de, después de…

(Practice and record yourself)

C. Rehearse several times.
Pay attention to your pronunciation—it will count toward your grade!
Repeat the words or sentences that are especially difficult for you.

D. Record your voice message.
Make sure that you record in a quiet place that is free from interruptions.

UNIDAD 5

Comunicación

LECCIÓN 1

INTERPERSONAL

5 **INTERPERSONAL WRITING**
You are going to write a comment about an article on Spanish breakfast.

Read the article

A. Underline information you can use to write your comment, and compare a Spanish breakfast to a typical breakfast in your country.
Is there anything that surprises you (food, quantity, schedule)?

DESAYUNAR EN ESPAÑA

Desayunar no significa lo mismo en todos los países. En general, los españoles desayunan entre las siete y las nueve de la mañana. Toman café o leche con chocolate y pan tostado (con mantequilla y mermelada o con aceite y jamón), galletas o cereales. Muchas personas beben también un jugo de naranja todas las mañanas.

Normalmente, en España desayunamos poca cantidad, y solo algunas personas toman un segundo (2.º) desayuno a media mañana. La causa es que, en España, el desayuno no es la comida principal: la comida principal es al mediodía, entre las dos y las tres de la tarde.

Write a comment

B. Write two or three complete sentences to share your opinion about the article.

Comentar

¡Hola! A mí me sorprenden (*I am surprised by*) muchas cosas del artículo.

Por ejemplo, los españoles desayunan muy poco. En mi país...

....

....

....

....

....

UNIDAD 5

El tiempo libre de los jóvenes

MI VOCABULARIO

1 EL TIEMPO LIBRE (1)

★ What do these young people do in their free time?
Write the activity under the corresponding picture.

~~ir al cine~~	chatear	salir a almorzar	hacer deporte
leer revistas	ir de compras	jugar a videojuegos	ir a un concierto
ver películas	leer libros	hacer compras en línea	ir al teatro

a

.... ir al cine ....

b

....

c

....

d

....

e

....

f

....

g

....

h

....

i

....

j

....

k

....

l

....

UNIDAD 5

El tiempo libre de los jóvenes

MI VOCABULARIO

2 **EL TIEMPO LIBRE (1)**

★★ **A. Place** each leisure activity in the most appropriate box according to internet usage.

navegar por internet   salir a cenar   escuchar música   salir con amigos/as

ver la televisión   leer cómics   ver series   ver videos

TIEMPO LIBRE CON INTERNET	TIEMPO LIBRE SIN INTERNET
navegar por internet, ...	

TIEMPO LIBRE CON Y SIN INTERNET

B. Place the leisure activities from activity 1 in the most appropriate box according to internet usage.

3 **LAS ESTADÍSTICAS**

★★★ **Look at** the infographic in the Student Edition about how Spanish teenagers spend their free time. **Write** three complete sentences using the data. **Use la mayoría de los / las** and **el ... por ciento de los / las**.

La mayoría de los jóvenes españoles...

....

....

....

....

UNIDAD 5

El tiempo libre de los jóvenes

LECCIÓN 2

MI GRAMÁTICA

4 EXPRESSING PREFERENCES

★ **Look at** each pair of emojis below. Which option do you prefer?
Write complete sentences using **prefiero... a...**

a. Prefiero jugar al... ....

a jugar al... ....

b. ....

....

c. ....

....

5 EXPRESSING PREFERENCES

★ What do these people prefer to do in their free time?
Complete the sentences with **preferir... a...**

a. Mi profesora prefiere leer libros a... ....

....

b. Mi mejor amigo y yo ....

....

c. Mi familia ....

....

d. Mis amigos ....

....

UNIDAD 5

Paseando por Madrid

MI VOCABULARIO

6 **EL TIEMPO LIBRE (2)**

★ **Read** these social media posts.
Reply to the questions using some of the words below.

corriendo   paseando   tomando una foto

leyendo   montando en patineta   paseando al perro

Adrián Ferreiro

a

♥ 532 Me gusta

¿Qué estoy haciendo?
#ahora

Comentarios:

Estás… ....

....

....

Eva Expósito

b

♥ 925 Me gusta

¿Qué estamos haciendo mi amiga Marta y yo? #ahora

Comentarios:

Marta y tú están… ....

....

....

Colegio Barcelonés

c

♥ 789 Me gusta

¿Qué están haciendo los estudiantes? #ahora

Comentarios:

Los estudiantes están…

....

....

7 **EL TIEMPO LIBRE (1 Y 2)**

★★ **Choose** three pictures of yourself, such as from your social networks.
In complete sentences, **describe** what you and / or your friends are doing in each picture.

a. En la foto 1, estoy… ....

....

b. En la foto 2, mis amigos y yo estamos… ....

....

c. En la foto 3, estoy / estamos… ....

....

UNIDAD 5

Paseando por Madrid

LECCIÓN 2

MI GRAMÁTICA

8 THE PRESENT PARTICIPLE

★★ **Write** the present participle of the verbs.
Then, **highlight** the irregular forms.

a. hablar → hablando

b. almorzar → ....

c. chatear → ....

d. dormir → ....

e. pasear → ....

f. ver → ....

g. ir → ....

h. leer → ....

i. jugar → ....

j. decir → ....

9 THE PRESENT PROGRESSIVE: ESTAR + PRESENT PARTICIPLE

★★★ **Read** the questions and **listen to** the voice messages.
Put a mark (✓) in the pictures that match the voice messages.
Then, **write** complete sentences to describe what these people are doing.

a. ¿Qué está haciendo Idoia?

1 ✓

Idoia está...

....

2

....

....

3

....

....

b. ¿Qué está haciendo Rosa?

1

....

....

2

....

....

3

....

....

c. ¿Qué está haciendo Jesús?

1

....

....

2

....

....

3

....

....

UNIDAD 5

Paseando por Madrid

MI GRAMÁTICA

10 **THE PRESENT PROGRESSIVE: ESTAR + PRESENT PARTICIPLE**

★★ **Compare** the two illustrations below and **spot** the six differences.
Then, **describe** the differences in complete sentences.

1. En la imagen A, Edu y Ana están corriendo. ....

En la imagen B, Edu y Ana están... ....

2. ....

....

3. ....

....

4. ....

....

5. ....

....

6. ....

....

UNIDAD 5

¿Dentro o fuera de las pantallas? ▬▬▬▬▬▬▬▬▬ LECCIÓN 2

MI VOCABULARIO

11 **LOS DISPOSITIVOS ELECTRÓNICOS**

★ **Identify** the six electronic devices.
Pay attention: There are four distractors!

1. ....
2. ....
3. ....
4. ....
5. ....
6. ....

TELEVISIÓNCELULARCUADERNOBOLÍGRAFOCOMPUTADORACONSOLATABLETAREVISTACÁMARADEFOTOSLIBRO

12 **LOS DISPOSITIVOS ELECTRÓNICOS**

★ **Look at** the picture. What electronic devices do you recognize?
Complete the crossword below and **guess** the hidden word (**?**).

```
            ?
            ▼
d ▸ L I B R O ▓ □ □ □ □ □ □ □ □ □
            Á
      b ▸ □ □ □ □ □ □ □ □ □
        a ▸ □ □ □ □ □
            R
    c ▸ □ □ □ □ □ □ □
```

UNIDAD 5

Copyright © by Difusión, S. L.

¿Dentro o fuera de las pantallas? ████████████████ LECCIÓN 2

MI VOCABULARIO

13 **LOS DISPOSITIVOS ELECTRÓNICOS**
★ **Unscramble** these words.

| E | T | V | I | L | Ó | N | I | E | S |

a. la ....

| C | A | L | O | S | O | N |

b. la ....

| A | R | Á | M | C | A | | E | D | | T | O | F | O | S |

c. la ....

| R | U | L | C | L | E | A |

d. el ....

14 **LOS DISPOSITIVOS ELECTRÓNICOS • RECUERDA: EL TIEMPO LIBRE (1 Y 2)**
★★★ **Answer** the questions with complete sentences.

1. ¿Cuál es tu dispositivo electrónico favorito? ¿Qué actividades haces con él?

....

....

2. ¿Qué dispositivo electrónico no usas normalmente? ¿Por qué?

....

....

UNIDAD 5

¿Dentro o fuera de las pantallas? ▰▰▰▰▰▰▰▰▰▰▰ LECCIÓN 2

MI GRAMÁTICA

15 **DIRECT OBJECT PRONOUNS**

★ **Match** the questions (**a–d**) with the corresponding answers (**1–4**).

a. ¿Dónde están mis libros?

b. ¿Dónde está mi celular?

c. ¿Dónde está mi computadora?

d. ¿Dónde están mis revistas?

1. La tengo yo; estoy viendo una serie.

2. Los tiene Margarita en su mochila.

3. Las tienes en tu habitación.

4. Lo tengo yo.

16 **DIRECT OBJECT PRONOUNS**

★★ **Read** the sentences and **look at** the underlined words.
Fill in the blanks with the correct direct object pronouns.

a. ¿Dónde están <u>mis lápices</u>? No ____los____ veo en el salón de clase.

b. Yo veo <u>muchas películas</u>. Normalmente _____ veo en la computadora.

c. Yo nunca me olvido de (forget) <u>mi celular</u>. Siempre _____ llevo encima.

d. <u>Estos cómics</u> me gustan mucho. ¿_____ conoces (know)?

e. A veces, tengo <u>muchas tareas</u>. Siempre _____ hago después de merendar.

f. Mi hermano tiene <u>una consola</u>. Yo a veces _____ uso para jugar con mis amigos.

17 **DIRECT OBJECT PRONOUNS • EXPRESSING PURPOSE:** **PARA** **+ INFINITIVE**

★★ **Answer** the questions in complete sentences.

ⓐ  ⓑ  ⓒ ⓓ  ⓔ

a. ¿Para qué usas los tenis? Los tenis, los uso para correr. ....

b. ¿Para qué usas los audífonos? ....

c. ¿Para qué usas el bolígrafo? ....

d. ¿Para qué usas la cámara de fotos? ....

e. ¿Para qué usas el libro? ....

UNIDAD 5

La vida en el celular

MI VOCABULARIO

18 EL TIEMPO LIBRE DIGITAL
★ **Fill in** the blanks with the missing vowels.

| | P | | G | | R |

| D | | R | | N | | M | | G | | S | T |

| C | | R | G | | R |

| N | V | | R | | N | | M | | N | S | | J |

19 EL TIEMPO LIBRE DIGITAL
★★ **Read** the definitions and **write** the corresponding verbs.

a. Conectar el celular. → **E** N C E N D E R

b. Enviar un mensaje a alguien que te escribe. → **R** ....

c. Desconectar el celular. → **A** ....

d. Compartir fotos en las redes sociales. → **S** ....

20 EL TIEMPO LIBRE DIGITAL
★★★ **Choose** three unit vocabulary items from this page.
Write three complete sentences about yourself.

a. Normalmente, enciendo mi celular por la mañana a las...

b. ....

c. ....

d. ....

UNIDAD 5

La vida en el celular

MI VOCABULARIO

21 EL TIEMPO LIBRE DIGITAL • RECUERDA: EL TIEMPO LIBRE (1 Y 2)

★ **A. Take** the test and **choose** the best answer for you.

🔊 **UNA VIDA SIN CONEXIÓN: ¿PUEDES VIVIR SIN CONEXIÓN?**

1. Vas a una isla desierta, ¿qué llevas *(take)***?**

○ **a.** El celular.

○ **b.** Un libro.

○ **c.** Un cuaderno.

2. ¿Qué haces cuando desayunas?

○ **a.** Miro el celular y leo los mensajes.

○ **b.** Veo la televisión.

○ **c.** Hablo con la familia.

3. ¿Qué prefieres hacer en tu tiempo libre?

○ **a.** Ver series y películas.

○ **b.** Leer libros, cómics o revistas.

○ **c.** Estar con mis amigos al aire libre.

4. ¿Cómo te comunicas con tu familia cuando estás lejos?

○ **a.** Envío mensajes con mi celular.

○ **b.** Llamo por teléfono.

○ **c.** Escribo una postal o una carta.

5. Antes de acostarte, ¿qué haces?

○ **a.** Miro el celular y mis redes sociales.

○ **b.** Veo una película o una serie.

○ **c.** Leo un libro, un cómic o una revista.

B. Check your answers and **read** your profile. Do you agree? Yes No

MAYORÍA DE RESPUESTAS ⓐ	**MAYORÍA DE RESPUESTAS ⓑ**	**MAYORÍA DE RESPUESTAS ⓒ**
No sabes *(you don't know)* qué hacer sin un celular o sin una computadora. No puedes vivir sin tener conexión a internet.	Usas las nuevas tecnologías, pero también te gusta leer, ver la televisión, hablar con tus familiares y salir con tus amigos y amigas.	Normalmente, no necesitas la tecnología en tu rutina diaria. Puedes vivir sin el celular. Te gustan los detalles, las cosas simples y cotidianas.

UNIDAD 5

La vida en el celular

MI GRAMÁTICA

22 IR A + INFINITIVE

★ **Complete** the sentences with the correct form of **ir**.

El fin de semana, ^a ....voy.... a estar en casa, con mi familia.

Por la mañana, ^d .... a estudiar Matemáticas.

Mis abuelos ^b .... a visitarnos el domingo.

Mi padre ^e .... a cocinar para todos.

Mis abuelos y yo ^c .... a ir al cine el domingo por la tarde.

Y tú, ¿qué ^f .... a hacer el fin de semana?

23 IR A + INFINITIVE

★★ **Complete** these dialogues with the correct verbs.
Use ir a + infinitive.

~~estudiar~~   almorzar   ir   jugar   hacer (x2)   ver   salir (x2)

a. ● ¡Hola, Laura! ¿Mañana por la tarde, ...vas a estudiar.... Matemáticas?

○ No, mañana .... al cine con mis abuelos.

b. ● Este fin de semana, mi familia y yo .... a almorzar a un restaurante. ¿Y ustedes, qué ....?

○ Nosotros .... en casa y luego .... una serie española: *La Casa de Papel*. ¿La conoces?

c. El sábado por la tarde, yo .... deporte en el parque. Después, mi hermano y yo .... a cenar juntos y, por la noche, ... a videojuegos en línea.

24 IR A + INFINITIVE

★★★ **Write** what you are going to do this weekend.

....
....

UNIDAD 5

Comunicación

INTERPRETIVE

1 INTERPRETIVE READING

You are going to read an article about teenagers and technology.

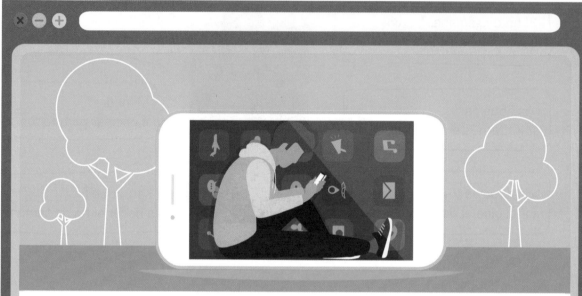

ADOLESCENTES SUPERCONECTADOS

Muchos adolescentes son dependientes de los dispositivos electrónicos, especialmente del teléfono celular. Además, las actividades más apreciadas en su tiempo libre son siempre actividades en internet.

Según el último informe de la OCDE[1] sobre el bienestar[2] de los estudiantes,
5 los estudiantes españoles están conectados aproximadamente tres horas entre semana (de lunes a viernes) y media hora más los fines de semana (sábados y domingos). Más datos: el 22 % de los adolescentes son usuarios extremos de internet, es decir, están más de seis horas conectados de lunes a viernes. ¿Y esto qué significa? Significa que tienen muy poco tiempo para otras actividades
10 mucho más saludables, como por ejemplo, hacer deporte, salir con amigos o estudiar. También tienen más probabilidades de suspender un examen y usar el celular en horario escolar.

En España, en la mayoría de los colegios de primaria y secundaria está prohibido usar el celular, pero muchos adolescentes lo usan. Para bastantes jóvenes, el
15 celular es el objeto más importante de sus vidas. Pero ¿por qué? Porque con este dispositivo electrónico pueden hacer muchas cosas: chatear, enviar mensajes, mirar las redes sociales, despertarse a tiempo por las mañanas, tomar fotos, jugar a videojuegos o ver series y películas en línea.

1 Organización Internacional para la Cooperación y el Desarrollo 2 well-being

UNIDAD 5

(Before reading)

A. Look at the illustration and **read** the title of the article on the previous page. What do you think the article is about?

....

(First reading)

B. Guess the meaning of these sentences from the article.

Put a mark (✓) in the correct option.

1. "Muchos adolescentes son dependientes de los dispositivos electrónicos".

   a. Muchos adolescentes son adictos a los dispositivos electrónicos. ☐

   b. Muchos adolescentes no usan los dispositivos electrónicos todos los días. ☐

2. "Un 22 % de los adolescentes son usuarios extremos de internet".

   a. Más de la mitad de los adolescentes de España usa mucho internet. ☐

   b. Una parte de los adolescentes usa internet más de seis horas por semana. ☐

3. "En España, en la mayoría de los colegios (...) está prohibido usar el celular".

   a. En España, los adolescentes pueden usar el celular en muchos colegios. ☐

   b. En muchos colegios españoles, los adolescentes no pueden usar el celular. ☐

4. "Para bastantes jóvenes, el celular es el objeto más importante de sus vidas".

   a. La mayoría de jóvenes españoles no puede vivir sin su celular. ☐

   b. Normalmente, los jóvenes españoles no usan el celular en su rutina diaria. ☐

(Second reading)

C. Answer the questions.

1. ¿Qué consecuencias puede tener ser un/a usuario/a extremo/a de internet? ....

....

2. ¿Para qué usan el celular los jóvenes españoles? ....

....

UNIDAD 5

Comunicación

INTERPRETIVE

2 **INTERPRETIVE LISTENING**
You are going to listen to a podcast from a high school about student leisure activities.

(Before listening)
A. Look at the pictures and **write** the term for each leisure activity.

1
salir con
amigos/as

2
....
....

3

....
....

4
....
....

5
....
....

6
....
....

7
....
....

8
....
....

🔊 (First listen)
B. What activities are mentioned in the podcast?
Put a mark (✓) in the pictures showing activities that are mentioned.

🔊 (Second listen)
C. Answer the questions.

1. ¿Por qué tiene poco tiempo libre el último *(last)* muchacho? ....

....

2. ¿Cuáles son las actividades preferidas de los estudiantes del colegio? ....

....

3. ¿Cuál es la conclusión del entrevistador? ....

....

UNIDAD 5

Comunicación

PRESENTATIONAL

3 PRESENTATIONAL WRITING

You are going to write a short article about how Spanish teenagers spend their free time.

(Before writing)

A. Read the infographic in the Student Edition about how Spanish teenagers spend their free time.

Write down in your notebook the information you find most interesting. You don't need to mention all the data in your article.

(Write the article)

B. Follow the structure.

Write a title for your article.

Answer these questions:

- ¿Qué actividades hacen los jóvenes españoles en su tiempo libre?

- ¿Coinciden con los jóvenes de tu país?

- ¿Crees que los jóvenes en el futuro van a usar más o menos la tecnología?

Creo que los jóvenes...

Share your opinion about their leisure activities.

UNIDAD 5

Comunicación

PRESENTATIONAL

4 **PRESENTATIONAL SPEAKING**
Imagine that you are a vlogger.
You are going to record a video about your plans for next weekend.

(Prepare your video)

A. Write a script.

1. **Explain** chronologically what activities (online and offline) you are going to do.

El sábado por la mañana, voy a...
Por la tarde...
Y por la noche...

2. **Mention** where you are going and if you are going alone or with someone:
voy a ir solo/a, **con mis amigos**, **con mi familia**, etc.

3. For the online activities, **say** which device you are going to use:
computadora, **celular**, **consola**, etc.

4. **Say goodbye** to your followers.
Ask them to like your video.

(Practice and record yourself)

B. Practice several times before recording.
It will help you speak naturally and avoid making mistakes.
Repeat the words or sentences that are especially
difficult for you.

C. Record your video.
Look at the camera to connect with your followers.
Make sure that you record in a quiet place
that is free from interruptions.

UNIDAD 5

Comunicación

LECCIÓN 2

INTERPERSONAL

5 **INTERPERSONAL WRITING**

You are going to reply to Lucía's social media posts and write a new one for her.

(Read Lucía's post)

A. Highlight the times of the posts and the questions Lucía asks.

Lucía García

Estoy desayunando cereales con fruta, ¡mmm, delicioso! 😋
Y tú, ¿qué estás haciendo?

08:15

Comentarios:

....

....

....

Lucía García

Mis amigas y yo estamos viendo la tele.
¿Qué estás haciendo tú con tus amigos/as?

10:30

Comentarios:

....

....

....

Lucía García

Mi hermana está estudiando y mi madre, trabajando. ¿Qué están haciendo tus familiares?

06:00

Comentarios:

....

....

....

(Reply to Lucía)

B. Reply to Lucía's posts above. **Answer** her questions according to the time of the post.

C. Write a new post for Lucía.

Tell her what you are going to do on Saturday evening and **ask** her about her plans.

El sábado por la noche, yo voy a...

....

....

....

UNIDAD 5

CULTURE QUIZ ✓

1 **¿Qué idiomas son oficiales en España?**

a. Solo el español. ☐

b. El español y también el catalán, el gallego y el vasco. ☐

Ola! Adeu!

2 **Los españoles se acuestan normalmente...**

a. antes de las 10:30 de la noche. ☐

b. después de las 10:30 de la noche. ☐

3 **¿Cuál de estos desayunos es tradicional en España?**

a. Los churros. ☐

b. Los cereales. ☐

c. El jugo de naranja. ☐

d. El queso. ☐

4 **¿Cuándo comen los españoles la merienda?**

a. Entre el desayuno y el almuerzo. ☐

b. Entre el almuerzo y la cena. ☐

5 **"El flamenco es un estilo de música, de baile y de canto".**

a. Verdadero. ☐

b. Falso. ☐

6 **"Solo los españoles juegan a la pelota vasca".**

a. Verdadero. ☐

b. Falso. ☐

7 **¿Cuáles de estos deportes son populares en España?**

a. El tenis. ☐

b. La lucha libre. ☐

c. El béisbol. ☐

d. El baloncesto. ☐

8 **La Masía es la academia formativa del...**

a. Real Madrid. ☐

b. Fútbol Club Barcelona. ☐

9 **"España no es un país turístico".**

a. Verdadero. ☐

b. Falso. ☐

10 **"España es el país de nacimiento de la lengua española".**

a. Verdadero. ☐

b. Falso. ☐

UNIDAD 5

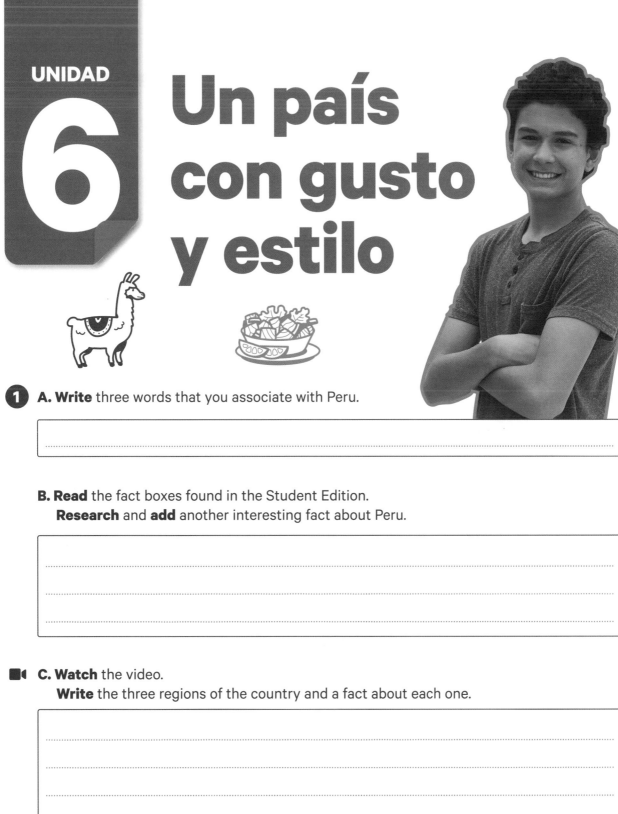

UNIDAD

6 Un país con gusto y estilo

1 **A. Write** three words that you associate with Peru.

B. Read the fact boxes found in the Student Edition.
   Research and **add** another interesting fact about Peru.

■◀ **C. Watch** the video.
   Write the three regions of the country and a fact about each one.

¿Qué ropa llevas?

MI VOCABULARIO

2 **LA ROPA • LOS ACCESORIOS**

★ **Write** the number of the corresponding item of clothing.

a. la chaqueta `6`

b. el vestido ☐

c. el gorro ☐

d. el abrigo ☐

e. los jeans ☐

f. el chaleco ☐

g. la gorra ☐

h. el pantalón corto ☐

i. el bolso ☐

j. el poncho ☐

k. la blusa ☐

l. las sandalias ☐

Copyright © by Difusión, S. L.

UNIDAD 6

¿Qué ropa llevas?

MI VOCABULARIO

3 LA ROPA • LOS ACCESORIOS

★ **Put a mark** (✓) for the clothing that is more appropriate for cold weather.

el suéter ☐

las medias ☐

las sandalias ☐

el gorro ☐

el pantalón corto ☐

el abrigo ☐

la chaqueta ☐

4 LA ROPA • LOS ACCESORIOS

★★★ **Look at** the illustration.
Read the descriptions. There are some mistakes.
Correct the descriptions to make them true.

Flor   María   Jorge

🔊

a Flor lleva una chaqueta, unos jeans y unos zapatos. También lleva unos aretes y un bolso.

b María lleva una falda, una chaqueta y unos tenis. No lleva accesorios.

c Jorge lleva unos jeans, una camisa y unas sandalias. También lleva lentes.

a. Flor lleva un suéter... ....

....

b. ....

....

c. ....

....

UNIDAD 6

¿Qué ropa llevas?

LECCIÓN 1

MI VOCABULARIO

5 LA ROPA • LOS ACCESORIOS
★★ **A. Write** the words for these clothing items and accessories.

.... la camiseta ....

🔊 **B. Listen to** Rubén and María's conversation.
Put a mark (✓) for the clothing and accessories Rubén could buy for his sister.

UNIDAD 6

Mi estilo, mi identidad

MI VOCABULARIO

6 **LOS ESTILOS (1)**

★ **Match** the name of the person who fits each description.

Ángel   Victoria   Luis   Rosa

a. Su estilo es casual. Lleva un pantalón corto muy cómodo. → ....

b. Lleva unas sandalias muy vistosas y un vestido elegante. → ....

c. Lleva una camiseta sencilla y unos jeans clásicos. ——→ ....

d. Su estilo es moderno. Lleva un pantalón muy original. ——→ ....

7 **LOS ESTILOS (1)**

★★ **Answer** the questions.

a. ¿Cómo es tu estilo? ....

....

b. ¿Qué ropa llevas normalmente? ¿Y los fines de semana? ....

....

....

c. ¿Cuál es tu prenda favorita? ¿Por qué? ....

....

UNIDAD 6

Mi estilo, mi identidad

LECCIÓN 1

MI VOCABULARIO

8 **LOS ESTILOS (1)**

★★ **Choose** the correct adjective for each sentence.

vistosos   incómodas   ~~sencilla~~   originales

clásico   moderno   elegante   deportiva

a. Siempre llevo ropa _____sencilla_____. La moda no es importante para mí.

b. Para el *Prom*, llevamos ropa _____. No podemos llevar ropa casual.

c. Llevo ropa _____ para jugar al béisbol: una sudadera y unos tenis.

d. Para mí, las faldas son _____. No puedo moverme (*move*) bien con ellas.

e. Normalmente, los adultos tienen un estilo más _____ y los jóvenes,

un estilo más _____.

f. Me gustan mucho los colores y siempre llevo tenis _____.

g. Siempre llevo camisetas _____. Me gusta ser diferente.

9 **LOS ESTILOS (2)**

★★ **Put a mark** (✓) in the correct option to finish each sentence.

a. Este año, mucha gente lleva ponchos.

Los ponchos...

1. van a la moda. ☐

2. están de moda. ☐

3. no tienen estilo. ☐

b. Mis papás no saben combinar la ropa.

Mis papás...

1. van a la moda. ☐

2. están de moda. ☐

3. no tienen estilo. ☐

c. Miguel y Fernando siempre llevan ropa moderna y original.

Miguel y Fernando...

1. van a la moda. ☐

2. están de moda. ☐

3. no tienen estilo. ☐

Copyright © by Difusión, S. L.

UNIDAD 6

Mi estilo, mi identidad

LECCIÓN 1

● **MI VOCABULARIO**

🔟 LOS ESTILOS (1 Y 2) • RECUERDA: LA ROPA Y LOS ACCESORIOS
★★★ What kinds of clothes are these people wearing? **Describe** their styles using adjectives. Note that you need to **make** the noun-adjective agreement.

a

Paula lleva <u>una falda elegante...</u>

....

....

....

....

....

b

Rodrigo lleva ....

....

....

....

....

....

c

Almudena lleva ....

....

....

....

....

....

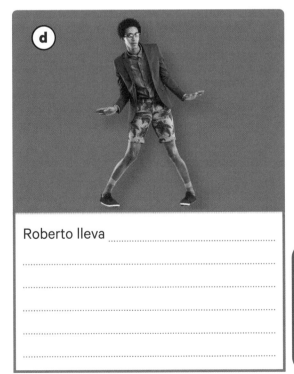

d

Roberto lleva ....

....

....

....

....

....

UNIDAD 6

¿Cuánto cuesta esta camiseta?

MI VOCABULARIO

11 **EN LA TIENDA DE ROPA** • **EL PRECIO**

★ **Match** the dialogues (**a–c**) with the correct illustrations (**1–3**).

🔊 **a** ☐

  o ¿Le queda bien? ¿Es su talla?
  • Me queda un poco pequeño.
    ¿Tiene una talla mediana?

b ☐

  • ¿Me puedo probar este suéter?
  o Claro, el probador está detrás
    de usted.

c ☐

  • ¿Cuánto cuesta? ¿60 soles?
  o No, está rebajado. Son 45 soles.

12 **EN LA TIENDA DE ROPA**

★★ **Complete** the conversation with the sentences below.

| ¿Lo tiene en otro color? | ~~Me puedo probar~~ | Me lo llevo. | ¿Cuál es su talla? |

| ¿Cuánto cuesta? | ¿Le queda bien? | ¿Puedo ver el negro? | Aquí lo tiene. |

Manuel: ¡Hola!, ¿ ª me puedo probar este pantalón rojo?

Dependienta: Sí, claro. **b** ....

Manuel: Mediana.

Dependienta: Este pantalón es de su talla.

Dependiente: **c** ....

Manuel: Sí, bien. **d** ....

Dependienta: Sí, lo tengo también en negro.

Manuel: **e** ....

Dependienta: Sí, claro. **f** ....

Manuel: Prefiero el pantalón rojo. **g** ....

Dependienta: El precio es 260 soles.

Manuel: Está bien. **h** ....

ESTRATEGIA 🔧

Practice with role-play

Role-play is a enjoyable way to practice your interpersonal speaking skills. In pairs, you can **act out a scene in a clothing store or some other kind of shop** and practice all the vocabulary you have learned.

UNIDAD 6

¿Cuánto cuesta esta camiseta? ▰▰▰▰▰▰ LECCIÓN 1

MI GRAMÁTICA

13 **DEMONSTRATIVES**

★ **Underline** the correct option for each demonstrative.

a. Este ⟶ **camisa** / **suéter** / **pulseras** / **lentes**

b. Estos ⟶ **abrigo** / **medias** / **falda** / **collares**

c. Esta ⟶ **gorra** / **tenis** / **camisas** / **suéter**

d. Estas ⟶ **lentes** / **vestido** / **sandalias** / **falda**

14 **DEMONSTRATIVES**

★★ **Read** the conversation between Carlos and Bea.
Underline the correct demonstrative.

Carlos: ¿Te gusta **este** / **ese** gorro azul?

Bea: Sí, pero me gusta más **este** / **ese** naranja que está en la pared.

Bea: ¿Cuánto cuestan **estos** / **esos** pantalones?

Carlos: ¿Cuáles? ¿**Estos** / **Esos**? Son muy caros.

Carlos: ¿Te gustan **estas** / **esas** medias azules?

Bea: Prefiero **estas** / **esas** verdes. Son más bonitas.

Bea: ¿Te gusta **esta** / **esa** sudadera verde?

Carlos: Me gusta más **esta** / **esa** azul de la pared.

UNIDAD 6

¿Cuánto cuesta esta camiseta?

MI GRAMÁTICA

15 DEMONSTRATIVES

★ **Complete** the sentences with **este**, **esta**, **estos**, or **estas**.

a. ¿Cuánto cuesta ..... este ..... collar?

b. .... ponchos son muy caros.

c. ¿Puedo probarme .... vestido?

d. ¿Te gustan .... sandalias?

e. ¿Tienen .... falda en otro color?

f. Mira .... zapatos. Son originales, ¿no?

16 QUESTION WORDS

★★ **Complete** the sentences with the correct question words.

Cuál   Cuánto   Dónde   Qué   ~~Cuáles~~   Por qué   Cuándo

a. ¿ ..... Cuáles ..... te gustan más: los zapatos rojos o los negros?

b. ¿ .... cuesta esta camisa?

c. ¿ .... abren las tiendas de ropa, a las 10 h o a las 11 h?

d. ¿ .... llevas en la mochila?

e. ¿ .... llevas lentes de sol? Estamos en la biblioteca.

f. ¿ .... está el probador?

g. ¿ .... es su talla?

17 QUESTION WORDS

★★ **Complete** the sentences with **cuánto/a/os/as** or **cuál/es**.

a. ¿ ..... Cuántos ..... pares de tenis tiene Juan José?

b. ¿ .... horas de clase por día tienes?

c. ¿ .... cuesta esta camiseta?

d. ¿ .... quieres, el abrigo rojo o el verde?

e. ● Me llevo estos lentes de sol.

　　○ ¿ ...., estos morados o esos azules?

ESTRATEGIA

Master the agreement

You already learned that in Spanish, you need to make the noun-adjective agreement. In order to help you master the agreement, **make a list of all the words** you have learned so far that **need to agree with the nouns they refer to**: adjectives, possessives, demonstratives, question words like **cuánto/a/os/as** and **cuál/es**. Write an example sentence for each kind of word.

UNIDAD 6

Un regalo para mis amigos

MI VOCABULARIO

18 **LOS NÚMEROS**

★★ **A. Listen** to the conversations.

🔊 **Write** the correct price for each item.

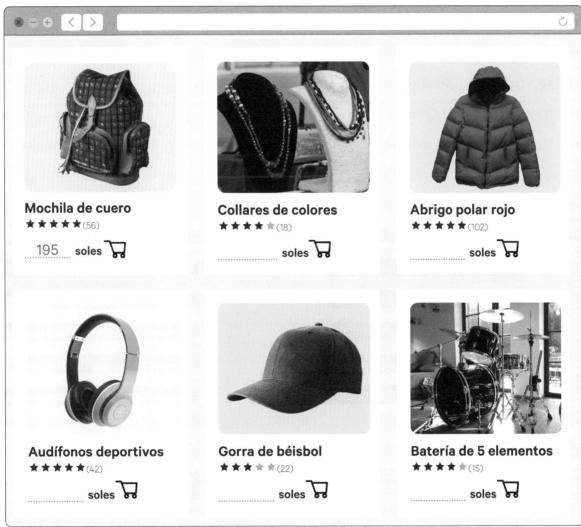

Mochila de cuero
★★★★★ (56)

195 **soles**

Collares de colores
★★★★☆ (18)

.... **soles**

Abrigo polar rojo
★★★★★ (102)

.... **soles**

Audífonos deportivos
★★★★★ (42)

.... **soles**

Gorra de béisbol
★★★☆☆ (22)

.... **soles**

Batería de 5 elementos
★★★★☆ (15)

.... **soles**

B. Spell out the prices.

1. La mochila cuesta ciento noventa y cinco soles. ....

2. Los collares cuestan ....

3. El abrigo cuesta ....

4. Los audífonos cuestan ....

5. La gorra cuesta ....

6. La batería cuesta ....

UNIDAD 6

Un regalo para mis amigos

LECCIÓN 1

MI VOCABULARIO

19 LOS NÚMEROS

★★ **Calculate** the sums.
Spell out the results.

a. **115 + 120 =** doscientos treinta y cinco ....

b. **212 + 238 =** ....

c. **550 + 363 =** ....

d. **478 + 214 =** ....

e. **605 + 395 =** ....

20 LAS TIENDAS

★ **Match** the beginnings of the sentences (**a–e**) with the endings (**1–5**).

a. Puedes comprar unos jeans...

b. Puedes comprar una guitarra...

c. Puedes comprar un celular...

d. Puedes comprar una pulsera...

e. Puedes comprar un balón de baloncesto...

1. ... en una tienda de deportes.

2. ... en una tienda de bisutería.

3. ... en una tienda de tecnología.

4. ... en una tienda de ropa.

5. ... en una tienda de música.

21 LAS TIENDAS

★ **Write** the word for the kind of store that corresponds to each description.
Note that you need to **put an accent mark** on one vowel of each word.

a. En esta tienda, venden sandalias. | Z | | | | | | | |

b. En esta tienda, venden chocolate. | C | | | | | | | | | | |

c. En esta tienda, venden libros. | L | | | | | | |

d. En esta tienda, venden plantas. | F | | | | | | | | |

Copyright © by Difusión, S. L.

UNIDAD 6

Un regalo para mis amigos

● **MI GRAMÁTICA**

22 INDIRECT OBJECT PRONOUNS

★ Andrés is cleaning out his closet and sorting his clothes.
Read his notes and the information about his family.
Say to whom he can give each piece of clothing.
Use the verb **regalar** with an indirect object pronoun.

ROPA QUE ME QUEDA APRETADA

ROPA QUE ME QUEDA GRANDE

ROPA QUE NO ME GUSTA

  Luis es su hermano mayor (older). **Siempre lleva ropa cómoda porque le gusta hacer deporte.**

 Román y Hugo son sus primos pequeños.

 Su papá tiene que comprar ropa para el invierno. Usa la misma (the same) **talla que Andrés.**

a. A Luis puede ....

b. A Román y a Hugo puede ....

c. A su papá puede ....

23 INDIRECT OBJECT PRONOUNS

★★★ **Fill in** the blanks with the correct indirect object pronouns.

 me   te   le   nos   les

a. ● Mañana es el cumpleaños de mi hermano.

○ ¿Por qué no .... compras una sudadera?

b. ● ¿Cómo me queda esta camiseta?

○ .... queda muy bien.

c. ● ¿Por qué no llevas nunca este suéter a clase?

○ Porque .... queda apretado.

d. ● No tenemos lápices de colores para dibujar.

○ Yo .... puedo dar mis lápices si quieren.

e. ● Tengo mucha ropa que no uso. ¿Qué puedo hacer?

○ .... puedes regalar a mi hermano y a mí la ropa de nuestra talla.

UNIDAD 6

Comunicación

INTERPRETIVE

1 **INTERPRETIVE READING**

You are going to read an article about sustainable fashion.

🔊 # Activistas de la moda

↑ Marina Testino (2020)

Hoy comprar ropa es barato. Compramos más ropa que antes, pero usamos menos. Este estilo de vida tiene consecuencias para el medio ambiente[1]. Por ejemplo,
5 para hacer un pantalón hay que utilizar 3000 litros de agua.

Marina Testino es activista "eco" en moda. Esta modelo y diseñadora peruana usa las redes sociales para
10 enviar mensajes sencillos: es importante cambiar[2] nuestras rutinas en moda para ayudar al medio ambiente.

¿Cómo puedes ayudar? Puedes comprar en tiendas de segunda mano[3], donde
15 hay ropa muy bonita y original. También puedes intercambiar la ropa que no usas con amigos. ¡Es muy divertido! Otra cosa que puedes hacer es transformar tu ropa: pintarla de otro color, incorporar decoraciones nuevas, etc. De esta forma[4], puedes tener una prenda diferente. Con estas acciones extendemos la vida de las prendas de ropa
20 y producimos menos ropa nueva.

1 environment   2 change   3 secondhand   4 In this way

UNIDAD 6

⬤

Before reading

A. Read the title of the article and **look at** the picture on the previous page.
What do you think this article is about?

1. Describe la moda del futuro en el Perú. ☐

2. Presenta a una diseñadora (*designer*)
comprometida con el medio ambiente (*environment*). ☐

B. How many paragraphs does the article have? **Number** the paragraphs in the article.

First reading

C. Indicate the paragraph from the article each statement corresponds to.

1. Usar ropa de otras personas es bueno para el medio ambiente.

Paragraph 1 ☐   Paragraph 2 ☐   Paragraph 3 ☐

2. No usamos toda la ropa que compramos.

Paragraph 1 ☐   Paragraph 2 ☐   Paragraph 3 ☐

3. Hay famosos que quieren una moda más ecológica.

Paragraph 1 ☐   Paragraph 2 ☐   Paragraph 3 ☐

Second reading

D. Correct these sentences according to the article.

1. Actualmente, la gente compra menos ropa que antes porque la ropa es muy cara.

....

2. Para hacer un pantalón, hay que usar poca agua.

....

3. Para Marina Testino, las rutinas en moda no tienen influencia en el medio ambiente.

....

4. Comprar mucha ropa nueva ayuda al medio ambiente.

....

UNIDAD 6

Comunicación

INTERPRETIVE

2 **INTERPRETIVE LISTENING**

You are going to listen to a podcast about fashion.

(Before listening)

A. Look at the pictures in activity B.
Describe the styles of these people. **Use** two adjectives.

El estilo de la muchacha 1 es... ....

El estilo de la muchacha 2 es... ....

El estilo del muchacho 3 es... ....

 (First listen)

B. Who are Percy, Lorena, and Teresa?
Write each person's name below his / her picture.

1 ....

2 ....

3 ....

(Second listen)

C. Who is making these statements: Percy, Lorena, or Teresa?
Put a mark (✓) for the speaker of each statement.

1. Me gustan los colores vibrantes. ⟶ | Percy ☐ | Lorena ☐ | Teresa ☐

2. Mi estilo es muy sencillo. ⟶ | Percy ☐ | Lorena ☐ | Teresa ☐

3. Llevo ropa que me queda grande. ⟶ | Percy ☐ | Lorena ☐ | Teresa ☐

4. Quiero expresar que soy diferente. ⟶ | Percy ☐ | Lorena ☐ | Teresa ☐

5. Para mí, la moda no es importante. ⟶ | Percy ☐ | Lorena ☐ | Teresa ☐

6. Me identifico con un género musical. → | Percy ☐ | Lorena ☐ | Teresa ☐

UNIDAD 6

Comunicación

PRESENTATIONAL

3 **PRESENTATIONAL WRITING**

You are going to write a post about young people's fashion in your community for your class blog.

(Before writing)

A. Read the texts by the **reporteros** in the Student Edition (activity 8).
They will help you write your post.

(Write the post)

B. Follow the structure.

Write a title. ————

....

Les voy a hablar de la moda de los jóvenes de mi comunidad.

Describe:
- your personal style.
- your favorite clothes.
- the style of your friends—is it similar to or different from yours?

Mi estilo es...

....

....

....

....

....

....

....

Describe:
- the uniforms of your school or the most popular clothes.
- the accessories the students wear.

En el colegio, los estudiantes llevamos...

....

....

....

....

Explain how important fashion is for the young people in your community.

Para los jóvenes de mi comunidad, la moda es...

....

....

....

....

UNIDAD 6

Comunicación

PRESENTATIONAL

4 PRESENTATIONAL SPEAKING

Imagine that you are a radio host.
You are going to describe a fashion show for a live broadcast.

(Prepare the broadcast)

A. Describe the fashion models below in your notebook: clothes, accessories, and style.

El / La modelo número 1 / 2 / 3 / 4 lleva...
Su estilo es...

↑ Fashion show of Lima Fashion Week (2017)

(Practice and record yourself)

B. Practice several times.
   Pay attention to your pronunciation—it will count toward your grade!
   Repeat the words or sentences that are especially difficult for you.

C. Record your broadcast.
   Make sure that you record in a quiet place that is free from interruptions.

UNIDAD 6

Comunicación

INTERPERSONAL

5 **INTERPERSONAL WRITING**
You are going to write a message to a secondhand shop.

(Read the post)

A. What can you buy in Roperos? ....

 Roperos

Roperos es una tienda de segunda mano *(secondhand)* en Lima. Puedes encontrar ropa y accesorios baratos en excelentes condiciones. ¿Qué necesitas *(need)*? Escríbenos para más información.

(Write your message)

B. Imagine that you are a student in Lima (Peru) and you need to buy some clothes. **Write** a message to the shop answering these questions.

- ¿Qué quieres comprar?
- ¿Cuál es tu talla?
- ¿Qué color o estilo te gusta?

C. Add some questions for the shop. For example:

- What is the price for one of the products you need?
- Where is the shop?

ESTRATEGIA

Take advantage of the input
You can use some vocabulary from the social media post: **necesitar** *(need)*, **en excelentes condiciones**, etc.

Responder a Roperos

¡Hola! Necesito...

....

....

....

....

....

UNIDAD 6

Alimentos peruanos

MI VOCABULARIO

1 LOS ALIMENTOS

★ **A. Write** the words below under the correct picture.

1. la banana	**5.** la piña	**9.** la leche	**13.** el arroz
2. el yogur	**6.** el azúcar	**10.** el maíz	**14.** el tomate
3. las papas	**7.** la lechuga	**11.** el pollo	**15.** el salmón
4. la carne	**8.** la zanahoria	**12.** el aceite	**16.** los huevos

a
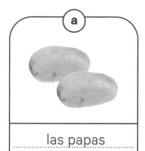
las papas

b

....

c
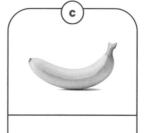
....

d
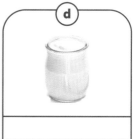
....

e

....

f
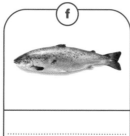
....

g

....

h

....

i

....

j
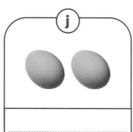
....

k
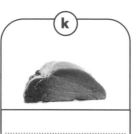
....

l

....

m

....

n

....

ñ

....

o

....

🔊 **B. Listen to** the voice message and **look at** the pictures above.
Circle the foods you hear mentioned.

UNIDAD 6

Alimentos peruanos LECCIÓN 2

MI VOCABULARIO

2 **LOS ALIMENTOS**

★ **Find** the odd one out in each series.

a. el yogur   el queso   el huevo   la leche

b. el salmón   el marisco   el atún   los frijoles

c. el aguacate   el atún   la carne   el pollo

d. la piña   el mango   la naranja   el queso

e. la cebolla   los dulces   la lechuga   la zanahoria

f. el maíz   la quinua   la manzana   el arroz   el pan

3 **LOS ALIMENTOS**

★ **Classify** the foods from activities 1 and 2 according to the following categories.

EL AZÚCAR Y LAS GRASAS
el azúcar, ...

LOS LÁCTEOS

LOS PRODUCTOS ANIMALES

LAS VERDURAS

LAS FRUTAS

LOS CEREALES, LOS TUBÉRCULOS Y LAS LEGUMBRES

UNIDAD 6

Alimentos peruanos

LECCIÓN 2

MI GRAMÁTICA

4 ADJECTIVES OF QUANTITY + NOUNS

★ **A. Look at** the Andean Peruvian food pyramid in the Student Edition.
Put a mark (✓) for the healthy eating habits.

1. Como muchas verduras. ☐
2. Como muy pocos cereales. ☐
3. Como bastantes legumbres. ☐
4. Como demasiados dulces. ☐
5. Bebo mucha leche. ☐
6. Bebo poca agua. ☐
7. Como poco pescado. ☐

B. Change the unhealthy habits to make them healthy.

Como muchos...

....

....

....

....

5 ADJECTIVES OF QUANTITY + NOUNS

★ **Look at** the Andean Peruvian food pyramid in the Student Edition.
Choose the appropriate adjective of quantity for each sentence.

bastante   pocos   muy pocas   muchas   mucha

Para llevar una dieta saludable *(healthy diet)*, tienes que...

a. comer _____muchas_____ frutas.

b. comer _____ pescado.

c. comer _____ grasas.

d. comer _____ huevos.

e. beber _____ agua.

UNIDAD 6

Yo como local ▬▬▬▬▬▬▬▬▬▬▬▬▬▬▬▬ LECCIÓN 2

MI VOCABULARIO

6 **TIPOS DE DIETA** • **RECUERDA: LOS ALIMENTOS**

★ **Find** four foods in each word search puzzle in order to complete the sentences.

a. Soy vegetariano/a. No puedo comer....

V	A	M	D	S	S	T	U	N
P	E	S	C	A	D	O	U	P
C	A	R	N	E	L	E	R	O
P	O	I	L	M	L	O	H	L
O	N	S	C	P	O	L	E	L
L	A	M	A	R	I	S	C	O

 1. pollo ....

 2. ....

 3. ....

 4. ....

b. Soy vegetariano/a. Sí puedo comer...

A	T	O	M	A	T	E	R	O
Y	A	P	E	S	D	P	Q	P
U	B	R	N	E	J	I	T	A
A	B	A	N	A	N	A	E	P
O	T	S	P	O	L	E	N	A
L	E	C	H	U	G	A	O	N

 1. ....

 2. ....

 3. ....

 4. ....

c. Soy intolerante al gluten y a la lactosa. No puedo comer o beber...

Q	G	A	L	O	P	T	A	U
U	M	R	E	L	E	P	N	G
E	A	G	C	A	N	A	O	U
S	T	S	H	O	L	N	G	R
O	Q	U	E	L	E	T	A	T
R	C	E	R	E	A	L	E	S

 1. ....

 2. ....

 3. ....

 4. ....

UNIDAD 6

Yo como local

MI VOCABULARIO

7 **TIPOS DE DIETA • RECUERDA: LOS ALIMENTOS**
★ **Put a mark** (✓) next to the correct food to complete each sentence.

a. Soy intolerante a la lactosa. No puedo comer....

tomate ☐   maíz ☐   quinua ☐   queso ☐

b. Soy alérgico/a al pescado. No puedo comer...

leche ☐   atún ☐   arroz ☐   huevos ☐

c. Soy vegetariano/a. No como...

carne ☐   naranjas ☐   zanahorias ☐   lechuga ☐

d. Soy diabético/a. No puedo comer mucho...

lechuga ☐   azúcar ☐   tomate ☐   frijoles ☐

8 **TIPOS DE COMIDA • TIPOS DE DIETA**
★ **Complete** the sentences with these words.

de todo   rápida   equilibrada   ~~chatarra~~   saludable

a. A Eva le encanta la comida ___chatarra___: hamburguesas,

papas fritas..., pero no es buena para la salud.

No es _____ .

b. Me gustan la carne, el pescado, las frutas, las verduras,

los cereales, las legumbres...

¡Como _____!

c. Me gusta llevar una dieta _____:

como alimentos diferentes para tener todos los nutrientes.

d. La comida _____ es una buena

opción cuando tienes poco tiempo.

ESTRATEGIA

Personalize to memorize
There are many ways to personalize the way you learn vocabulary for food. Try writing a **menu** of what you have eaten this week or write the menu for next week. You could also create **your own nutritional pyramid** with the food you eat more often at the bottom and the food you hardly ever eat at the top.

UNIDAD 6

Yo como local ████████████████████████ LECCIÓN 2

● **MI GRAMÁTICA**

9 **RECUERDA: ADVERBS OF FREQUENCY**
★★ **Look at** María Elena's diet.
Underline the correct option for each sentence.

a. **fruta**
lunes, martes, miércoles, jueves, viernes, sábado, domingo

e. **pollo**
miércoles, viernes

b. **verdura**
lunes, miércoles, viernes, sábado

f. **pescado**
martes, jueves, sábado

c. **arroz**
martes, miércoles, viernes

g. **leche**
un día por mes

d. **huevos**
un día por mes

h. **chocolate**
0 (no le gusta)

a. María Elena come fruta **<u>todos los días</u> / a veces / casi nunca**.

b. María Elena come verdura **todos los días / a menudo / casi nunca**.

c. María Elena come arroz **nunca / tres veces por semana / siempre**.

d. María Elena come huevos **siempre / todos los días / a veces**.

e. María Elena come pollo **todos los días / dos veces por semana / casi nunca**.

f. María Elena come pescado **siempre / casi nunca / tres veces por semana**.

g. María Elena **a menudo / todos los días / casi nunca** bebe leche.

h. María Elena **siempre / nunca / a veces** come chocolate.

10 **RECUERDA: ADVERBS OF FREQUENCY • RECUERDA: QUANTIFIERS**
★★ **Match** the beginings of the dialogues (**a–f**) with the endings (**1–6**).

a. Bebo un litro de leche por día.

b. Bebo agua dos veces por semana.

c. Tomo bebidas con azúcar todos los días.

d. Como tomates una vez por mes.

e. Como 20 dulces por día.

f. Como carne todos los días.

1. Comes muy pocos.

2. Bebes demasiadas.

3. No bebes mucha.

4. Comes demasiados.

5. Bebes mucha.

6. Comes mucha.

UNIDAD 6

La cuenta, por favor

MI VOCABULARIO

11 **EN EL RESTAURANTE (1 Y 2) • LAS SENSACIONES**
★★ **Complete** the crossword puzzle.

a. Plato, generalmente fruta o dulces, que comemos al final de una comida.

b. Tienes esta sensación cuando quieres comer: tienes…

c. Persona que come en un restaurante.

d. Antes del segundo plato, comemos el…

e. Mujer que trabaja en un restaurante. Sirve *(she serve)* la comida.

f. La Inca Kola es una … peruana.

g. Tienes esta sensación cuando quieres beber: tienes…

Crossword:
Vertical a: P O S T R E

12 **EN EL RESTAURANTE (1 Y 2)**
★ **Number** (**1–6**) these elements of a conversation between two customers and a waitress so that they are in the correct order.

 a
- ○ Tengo los aperitivos y los segundos. ¿Y para beber?
- ● Para mí, un agua sin gas, por favor.
- – Para mí, una chicha morada.

b
- ○ Perfecto. ¿Y de segundo?
- ● Para mí, pescado frito.
- – Para mí, arroz chaufa.

 c
- ● Buenos días. La carta, por favor.
- ○ Sí, claro. Aquí tienen.

d
- ○ ¿Qué desean de aperitivo?
- ● Para mí, patacones con salsa.
- – Para mí, una ensalada de pollo.

 e
- ○ Aquí tienen. ¡Buen provecho!
- ● Muchas gracias.

f
- ● ¡La cuenta, por favor!
- ○ Aquí tienen. Son 62 soles.

UNIDAD 6

La cuenta, por favor

MI VOCABULARIO

13 **EN EL RESTAURANTE (1 Y 2)**

★ **Complete** the dialogue with these words.

> de postre   la carta   qué lleva   de aperitivo
>
> la cuenta   de segundo   buen provecho   para beber

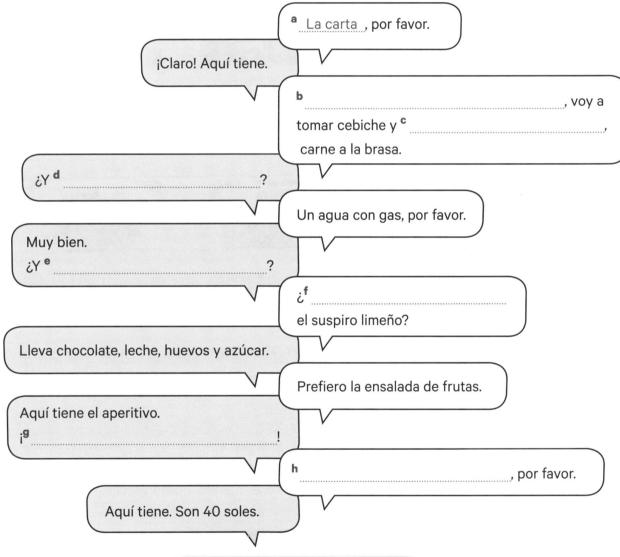

a La carta , por favor.

¡Claro! Aquí tiene.

b ...., voy a tomar cebiche y **c** ...., carne a la brasa.

¿Y **d** ....?

Un agua con gas, por favor.

Muy bien.
¿Y **e** ....?

¿ **f** .... el suspiro limeño?

Lleva chocolate, leche, huevos y azúcar.

Prefiero la ensalada de frutas.

Aquí tiene el aperitivo.
¡ **g** ....!

h ...., por favor.

Aquí tiene. Son 40 soles.

UNIDAD 6

La cuenta, por favor

MI VOCABULARIO

14 **EN EL RESTAURANTE (1 Y 2)** • **RECUERDA: LOS ALIMENTOS**

★ Andrés's family is eating out at a restaurant.
Look at the menu and **read** the information about their food preferences.
Choose the appropriate dishes for each person.

APERITIVOS

χ Ensalada de salmón y aguacate

χ Cebiche de marisco con cebolla y lechuga

χ Papas a la huancaína: crema de queso, leche y ají *(chili peper)*

SEGUNDOS

χ Pollo a la brasa con lechuga y tomate

χ Arroz con verduras variadas (con mucha cebolla)

χ Sopa de mariscos con pasta de trigo *(wheat)*

a. A **Andrés** le gustan mucho el pescado y la carne. No le gusta el tomate ni el aguacate. Es intolerante al gluten y no puede comer pasta normal.

De aperitivo va a tomar: _cebiche de marisco_

De segundo va a tomar: ....

b. La **mamá de Andrés** es vegetariana, pero come huevos, queso y leche.

De aperitivo va a tomar: ....

De segundo va a tomar: ....

c. El **hermano de Andrés** es intolerante a la lactosa. Prefiere el pescado a la carne o el pollo. Le gusta la verdura, pero no come cebolla.

De aperitivo va a tomar: ....

De segundo va a tomar: ....

UNIDAD 6

Cocina peruana

MI VOCABULARIO

15 **RECUERDA: LOS ALIMENTOS**

★ **A. Complete** the words to find out the main ingredient for these Peruvian dishes.

1 TACU TACU	2 CEBICHE	3 CAUSA LIMEÑA
A R R O Z	E S _ _ _ O	G U _ _ T _

4 JUANE	5 OCOPA	6 PARIHUELA
_ O L _	_ _ P A	M _ _ I S _

🔊 **B. Listen to** six people talking about these dishes.
Write all the ingredients they mention.

1. Tacu tacu → ....

2. Cebiche → ....

3. Causa limeña → ....

4. Juane → ....

5. Ocopa → ....

6. Parihuela → ....

UNIDAD 6

NAME .... CLASS .... DATE ....

Cocina peruana

LECCIÓN 2

MI VOCABULARIO

16 **RECUERDA: LOS ALIMENTOS Y EN EL RESTAURANTE (2)**

★ Your school's restaurant wants to honor Peruvian cuisine.
Create a Peruvian menu for three days.

Lunes	Aperitivo: Cebiche de pescado y marisco
	Segundo:
	Postre:
Martes	Aperitivo:
	Segundo:
	Postre:
Miércoles	Aperitivo:
	Segundo:
	Postre:

17 **RECUERDA: LLEVAR**

★ **Llevar** can be used in different contexts.
Look at some frequent word combinations (**a–e**) with **llevar**.
Write each sentence beside its corresponding word combination.

> **ESTRATEGIA**
>
> **Activate your vocabulary**
> Learning **frequent word combinations**, known as "chunks," will help you memorize new words and better organize the information.

Lleva un suéter rojo. Lleva barba. Lleva aretes.
Lleva pescado. Lleva una dieta equilibrada.

a. una comida llevar > un ingrediente ....

b. una persona llevar > un tipo de dieta ....

c. una persona llevar > una prenda de ropa ....

d. una persona llevar > un accesorio ....

e. una persona llevar > una característica física ....

Copyright © by Difusión, S. L.

UNIDAD 6

Cocina peruana

MI GRAMÁTICA

18 THE PRETERITE TENSE: REGULAR FORMS

★ **Conjugate** the verbs in the preterite tense.

	HABLAR	BEBER	ESCRIBIR
yo	hablé	beb	escrib
tú	habl	beb	escrib
él / ella, usted	habl	beb	escrib
nosotros/as	habl	beb	escrib
vosotros/as	habl	beb	escrib
ellos / ellas, ustedes	habl	beb	escrib

19 THE PRETERITE TENSE: REGULAR AND SOME IRREGULAR FORMS

★★ **Complete** the email with the correct preterite tense form of the verbs in parentheses. There is only ONE irregular verb.

Para: Macarena   Cc Bcc

Asunto: Restaurante peruano

Hola, ¿qué tal?

Ayer, Natalie y John **(ver)** ^a .... vieron .... un comercial en la tele de un restaurante peruano y, por la tarde, mis amigos y yo **(ir)** ^b .... al restaurante.

Cuando nosotros **(llegar)** ^c .... al restaurante, la mesera **(abrir)** ^d .... todas las ventanas. ¡Es julio y hace mucho calor!

Los meseros son peruanos. Yo **(hablar)** ^e .... español con ellos todo el tiempo. Natalie y Emily **(comer)** ^f .... causa limeña con bonito. Yo **(comer)** ^g .... lomo saltado.

Y John **(comer)** ^h .... patacones con salsa porque es vegetariano.

Todos nosotros **(beber)** ⁱ .... chicha morada.

El restaurante está muy bien. Todos queremos volver.

                ♀ ☆ 🛢 A   Enviar

UNIDAD 6

Comunicación

1 **INTERPRETIVE READING**

You are going to read a text about a Peruvian chef.

🔊 GASTÓN ACURIO, UN CHEF PERUANO MUY INTERNACIONAL

Gastón Acurio es un chef peruano muy conocido internacionalmente. Tiene más de 40 restaurantes
5   en todo el mundo. En sus restaurantes ofrece platos peruanos. Para Gastón Acurio, la gente puede conocer el Perú a través[1]
10 de sus restaurantes.

Astrid & Gastón fue su primer restaurante. Lo abrió en Lima, en 1994, con su esposa Astrid Gutsche, que también es cocinera de profesión.
15 Hoy es uno de los restaurantes más apreciados del mundo.

En 2002, grabó su primer programa de televisión: *Aventura Culinaria*. Este programa fue muy popular en el Perú. Luego, en 2003, escribió su primer libro: *Perú, una aventura culinaria*. En 2007, creó la Escuela de Cocina de Pachacútec. En esta escuela pueden estudiar muchos jóvenes
20 peruanos con bajos recursos[2].

1 through   **2** low-income

UNIDAD 6

LECCIÓN 2

(Before reading)

A. Look at the text.
   What text type is it?

   1. An email. ☐   **2.** An extract of a novel. ☐   **3.** An article. ☐

(First reading)

B. Decide whether the sentences are true (**T**) or false (**F**) according to the text.
Correct the false information.

   1. Gastón Acurio es un cocinero poco conocido. T F

   ....

   2. Gastón Acurio solo tiene restaurantes en el Perú. T F

   ....

   3. En los restaurantes de Gastón Acurio podemos comer comida peruana. T F

   ....

   4. Gastón Acurio abrió su primer restaurante solo. T F

   ....

   5. Gastón Acurio ayuda a jóvenes con problemas económicos. T F

   ....

(Second reading)

C. Complete these sentences with the correct information according to the text.

   1. En 1994, Gastón Acurio _abrió..._

   2. En 2002, Gastón Acurio ....

   ....

   3. En 2003, Gastón Acurio ....

   ....

   4. En 2007, Gastón Acurio ....

   ....

UNIDAD 6

Comunicación

INTERPRETIVE

2 **INTERPRETIVE LISTENING**
You are going to listen to a conversation in a restaurant.

Before listening

A. Read the menu in activity B.
It will help you better understand the audio track.

🔊 **First listen**

B. Put a mark (✓) next to the food and beverages the customers order.

MESA 4   ✕

APERITIVO
1. Cebiche de pescado ☐
2. Ensalada de marisco ☐
3. Ensalada de pollo ☐
4. Patacones con salsa ☐

SEGUNDO
1. Pescado frito ☐
2. Causa limeña con bonito ☐
3. Carne a la brasa ☐
4. Arroz chaufa ☐

BEBIDA
1. Agua con o sin gas ☐
2. Inca Kola ☐
3. Chicha morada ☐

POSTRE
1. Torta de tres leches ☐
2. Ensalada de frutas ☐
3. Yogur con frutas ☐

🔊 **Second listen**

C. Write what the woman and the man order.

De aperitivo, la mujer quiere...

....

....

....

....

....

D. Answer these questions.

1. ¿Qué alimento no le gusta al hombre? ....

2. ¿A qué alimento es alérgica la mujer? ....

UNIDAD 6

Comunicación

PRESENTATIONAL

3 PRESENTATIONAL WRITING

You are going to write a short article for *Somos reporteros* about the eating habits of young people in your school.

(Write the article)

A. Use the questions below to help you organize the information.

- ¿Comen muchas o pocas frutas y verduras?
- ¿Comen muchos o pocos productos con azúcar o grasa?
- ¿Cuántas veces por semana comen comida chatarra?
- ¿Beben mucha agua o prefieren bebidas con azúcar?
- ¿El comedor de tu colegio tiene un menú saludable?
- ¿Cuáles son las intolerancias o alergias alimentarias más frecuentes?

B. Add a sentence to say if you think the young people's diet is balanced or not. **Explain** why.

Los jóvenes de mi colegio comen...

(After writing)

C. Proofread your article.

Correct any mistakes you may find.

UNIDAD 6

Comunicación

PRESENTATIONAL

4 PRESENTATIONAL SPEAKING

You are going to record a podcast to encourage children to follow a healthy diet.

(Prepare the podcast)

A. Look at the Andean Peruvian food pyramid in the Student Edition.

B. Write the script in your notebook.

1. Explain what types of food they should eat every day.

Para comer más saludable, tienes que...
Por ejemplo...

2. Say what foods they shouldn't eat very often.

No tienes que comer demasiados...

3. Say how often they should have meat, fish, dairy, and eggs.

... veces por semana debes...

(Practice and record yourself)

C. Practice several times.
Pay attention to your pronunciation—it will count toward your grade!
Repeat the words or sentences that are especially difficult for you.

D. Listen to your recording before submitting your work.

- Have you included all the information in activity B? [Yes] [No]
- Have you checked the noun-quantifiers agreement? [Yes] [No]
- Is your pronunciation clear? [Yes] [No]
- Is the sound quality good enough? [Yes] [No]

E. Record the podcast again if needed.

UNIDAD 6

Comunicación

LECCIÓN 2

INTERPERSONAL

5 INTERPERSONAL WRITING

Your school is preparing a Festival of Cultures.
You are going to reply to an email from your Spanish teacher.

(Read your teacher's email)

A. Highlight the questions that your teacher asks.

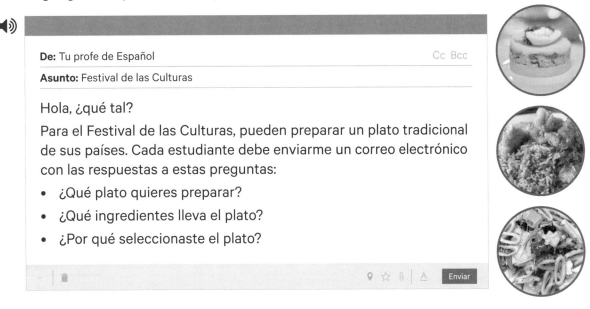

De: Tu profe de Español   Cc Bcc

Asunto: Festival de las Culturas

Hola, ¿qué tal?

Para el Festival de las Culturas, pueden preparar un plato tradicional de sus países. Cada estudiante debe enviarme un correo electrónico con las respuestas a estas preguntas:

- ¿Qué plato quieres preparar?
- ¿Qué ingredientes lleva el plato?
- ¿Por qué seleccionaste el plato?

Enviar

(Write your reply)

B. You need to **answer** all of your teacher's questions in your email.

Hola, ¿qué tal?

Para el Festival de las Culturas, yo quiero preparar...

Enviar

UNIDAD 6

CULTURE QUIZ

1 **¿Cuál es la capital del Perú?**

a. Quito. ☐

b. Lima. ☐

c. Bogotá. ☐

2 **¿Cuáles de estos sitios turísticos están en el Perú?**

a. El Machu Picchu. ☐

b. La Alhambra. ☐

c. El cañón de Cotahuasi. ☐

3 **"La tradición de tejer en el Perú es muy antigua".**

a. Verdadero. ☐

b. Falso. ☐

4 **¿Cuál es la moneda del Perú?**

a. El peso. ☐

b. El euro. ☐

c. El sol. ☐

5 **"El nombre de la moneda del Perú es el nombre de un dios Inca".**

a. Verdadero. ☐

b. Falso. ☐

6 **¿Cuáles de estos ingredientes lleva el cebiche?**

pescado crudo   arroz

limón   papas   maíz

cebolla   plátano

7 **¿Qué es la maca?**

a. Una fruta. ☐

b. Una verdura. ☐

c. Un tubérculo. ☐

8 **¿Qué es la quinua?**

a. Una fruta. ☐

b. Un cereal. ☐

c. Una verdura. ☐

9 **¿Cuáles de estos platos son típicos del Perú?**

a. La paella. ☐

b. El tiradito. ☐

c. El juane. ☐

10 **"Nikkei" significa descendiente de...**

a. europeos. ☐

b. japoneses. ☐

c. peruanos. ☐

UNIDAD 6

Text Credits

Unidad 1 p. 57 El Orden Mundial, IPUMS USA

Unidad 4 p. 159 Instituto Cervantes, 2020

Unidad 5 p. 178 Lourdes Miquel, Difusión, 2014

Photography Credits

¡EMPEZAMOS! p. 4 Bruna Prado/Getty Images, MikeVanSchoonderwalt/iStock, anharris/iStock, Damocean/iStock, grandriver/iStock, NASA, Sam Wasson/Getty Images; **p. 5** Instants/iStock, Juni Samos/iStock, gcoles/iStock, THEPALMER/iStock, Larysa Lyundovska/iStock, Jerónimo Alba/Alamy, SeanPavonePhoto/iStock, Natalie_/iStock; **p. 8** Classic Image/Alamy; **p. 11** SatapornJiwjalaen/Dreamstime, ValeriiZan/Dreamstime; **p. 12** chokkicx/iStock; **p. 13** dikobraziy/iStock; **p. 15** PeterHermesFurian/iStock; **p. 16** arquiplay77/iStock; **p. 17** Mosutatsu/iStock, Tonkovic/iStock, Fototocam/iStock, Vykkdraygo/Dreamstime, nata777_7/Adobe Stock, Michael Burrell/iStock, Picsfive/iStock, Design56/Dreamstime, dejan Jekic/iStock, Volodymyr Kotoshchuk/iStock, Jasmina81/iStock, archideaphoto/iStock, rclassenlayouts/iStock, stocksnapper/iStock, mrod/iStock; **p. 18** visualspace/iStock, kate_sept2004/iStock, RgStudio/iStock, FangXiaNuo/iStock, JackF/iStock, fizkes/iStock; **p. 19** cultura/iStock, JohnnyGreig/iStock, DMEPhotography/iStock, urbazon/iStock, ferrantraite/iStock, orijinal/dreamstime; **p. 20** OSTILL/iStock, PalosVerdesBlue/iStock, PRISMA ARCHIVO/Alamy, R.M. Nunes/iStock

Unidad 1 p. 22 Tashi-Delek/iStock, SDIProductions/iStock, vitapix/iStock, Prostock-Studio/iStock, fizkes/iStock, RobertKneschke/Dreamstime; **p. 23** fizkes/iStock, nullplus/iStock, Ridofranz/iStock, laflor/iStock; **p. 27** chode/Dreamstime; **p. 30** FGTrade/iStock; **p. 31** Donald Cooper/Alamy, RichPolk/Getty Images, CRIS BOURONCLE/Getty Images, NASA, NASA/Bill Ingalls, BobDaemmrich/Alamy; **p. 32** Astrid Stawiarz/Getty Images, macrovector/Freepik, Sbukley/Dreamstime, Julio Aguilar/Getty Images, AllstarPictureLibraryLtd/Alamy; **p. 34** Blackzheep/Dreamstime, EveOrea/Dreamstime, BurtJohnson/Dreamstime, HerySiswanto/Dreamstime, monkeybusinessimages/iStock, IrinaBrester/Dreamstime, LiliGraphie iStock, Milton Glaser; **p. 36** shironocov/iStock; **p. 38** VolodymyrMelnyk/Dreamstime; **p. 40** KavalenkavaVolha/iStock, Slobodeniuk/iStock, william87/iStock, Willbrasil21/iStock; **p. 41** Tartilastock/Dreamstime; **p. 42** Rawpixel/AdobeStock; **p. 44** Dean Mouhtaropoulos/Getty Images, Pascal Le Segretain/Getty Images, Layne

Murdoch Jr./Getty Images, John Phillips/Getty Images, NASA, Gustavo Caballero/Getty Images, dikobrazik/Fotolia; **p. 46** RossHelen/iStock, FGTrade/iStock, Liberty/iStock, frantic00/iStock, CarolineBrundleBugge/iStock, LSOphoto/iStock; **p. 47** laurareyero/iStock, Sean Pavone/iStock, Juergen Sack/iStock, Pgiam/iStock, Washington/iStock, lechatnoir/iStock; **p. 51** JohnPhillips/Getty Images; **p. 52** Starstock/Dreamstime, Featureflash/Dreamstime; **p. 54** reddees/iStock; **p. 56** SergiyPalamarchuk/Dreamstime; **p. 57** DmytroKozyrskyi/Dreamstime; **p. 58** pop_jop/iStock, maogg/iStock, © Terry Blas

Unidad 2 p. 60 Aamulya/iStock; **p. 61** FatCamera/iStock, fizkes/iStock, Pixel Pig/iStock, FreshSplash/iStock, Musica/iStock, Emanuele Capoferri/Adobe Stock; **p. 63** vgajic/iStock, PamelaJoeMcFarlane/iStock, DarioGaona/iStock, PeopleImages/iStock, Bim/iStock, LightFieldStudios/iStock; **p. 64** RicardoImagen/iStock; **p. 66** AntonVieirietin/iStock, Lepro/iStock; **p. 67** EricIsselee/Adobe Stock, LeonidNyshko/Adobe Stock; **p. 68** Winfield D Rosario/iStock; **p. 69** Columbia Pictures/Entretenimiento Fotos/Alaymy; **p. 70** EthanMiller/Getty Images, KevinWinter/Getty Images, RebeccaSapp/Getty Images, Victor Chavez/Getty Images; **p. 71** Grafner/Dreamstime, wundervisuals/iStock, Isselee/Dreamstime, VvoeVale/iStock, Difusión, Destina156/Dreamstime, pepifoto/iStock; **p. 72** ThomasNorthcut/iStock; **p. 74** mixetto/iStock; **p. 75** Edgardo Miranda-Rodríguez/Somos Arte; **p. 76** Hiraman/iStock; **p. 77** JessWealleans/iStock; **p. 78** SensorSpot/iStock, Koldunov/iStock, diego_cervo/iStock, FG Trade/iStock, Juanmonino/iStock, MilicaStankovic/iStock, Wpadington/iStock; **p. 80** Seventy Four/iStock; **p. 81** TheoWargo/Getty Images, Michael Tullberg/Getty Images, Frazer Harrison/Getty Images, David Livingston/Getty Images, Joe Scarnici/Getty Images, Mike Coppola/Getty Images, AmySussman/Getty Images, Amanda Edwards/Getty Images, Matt Winkelmeyer/Getty Images, JonKopaloff/Getty Images, JieXu/Dreamstime, RichFury/Getty Images, WENN Rights Ltd/Alamy; **p. 82** digitalskillet/iStock, MonkeyBusinessImages/Dreamstime, martinedoucet/iStock, Wellsie82/Dreamstime; **p. 84** nilimage/iStock, sv_sunny/iStock; **p. 85** 99roberto99/Wikimedia Commons, Sergi Alexander , SlavenVlasic/Getty Images; **p. 86** Hutchinsphoto/Dreamstime, GladysVega/Getty Images; **p. 87** VladimirYudin/Dreamstime; **p. 90** WeekendImagesInc/iStock; **p. 96** Saul Herrera/iStock, WM/iStock, Luis Alejandro Rodríguez Ortiz, SCHOMBURG: THE MAN WHO BUILT A LIBRARY. Text copyright © 2017 by Carole Boston Weatherford. Illustrations copyright © 2017 by Eric Velasquez. Reproduced by permission of the publisher, Candlewick Press.

Créditos

Unidad 3 p. 98 LisaStrachan/iStock, Kropic/Dreamstime, JoaquinCorbalan/Dreamstime, JoseAntonioNocoli/Dreamstime, Inna Luzan/iStock, Izanbar/Dreamstime, MediaRawStock/iStock, cesarhgv/iStock, Julioaldana/Dreamstime; **p. 99** Imke Zijm/Alamy, Pascopix/Alamy, Sergio Azenha/Alamy, Roberto Michel/iStock; **p. 100** redtea/iStock; **p. 101** snorkulencija/iStock; **p. 103** AnatoliyKashuba/Dreamstime; **p. 105** narawon/iStock; **p. 107** Loopall/Dreamstime, Ovydyborets/Dreamstime, Sgoodwin4813/Dreamstime, Ivictorkiev/Dreamstime, DejchgornChaimee/Dreamstime, BjornHovdal/Dreamstime, Maryna Riazanska/Dreamstime; **p. 108** goir/Dreamstime, Ambiente Mexicano, wacomka/iStock, Vitaliy Halenov/iStock, hudiemm/iStock, SutidaS/iStock, AlxMendezR/iStock, KatarzynaBialasiewicz/Dreamstime, Elizabeth Whiting & Associates/Alany; **p. 110** AlexandraDraghici/iStock, AaronAmat/iStock, Ridofranz/iStock, RobertDaly/iStock; **p. 111** FatCamera/iStock, JohnnyGreig/iStock; **p. 112** ManavLohia/Dreamstime; **p. 113** Sezeryadigar/iStock; **p. 114** kamil/iStock; **p. 116** richjem/iStock, RonTech2000/iStock; **p. 117** KatarzynaBialasiewicz/iStock; **p. 118** Katarzyna Bialasiewicz/iStock; **p. 119** Prostock-Studio/iStock, MesquitaFMS/iStock, yacobchuk/iStock, SolStock/iStock, franckreporter/iStock, urbazon/iStock; **p. 122** filo/iStock, gmast3r/iStock, Artis777/iStock; **p. 123** nerudol/iStock, LARISA SHPINEVA/iStock, Wavebreakmedia/iStock, chee gin tan/iStock, JadeThaiCatwalk/iStock, People Images/iStock; **p. 126** motortion/Dreamstime; **p. 127** Odua/Dreamstime; **p. 128** MesquitaFMS/iStock; **p. 130** macrovector/Freepik; **p. 131** Nevodka/Dreamstime; **p. 132** DMEPhotography/iStock; **p. 133** RickBL/iStock; **p. 134** Javier Senosiain Aguilar, Frida Kahlo, VEGAP/Album

Unidad 4 p. 136 mathisworks/iStock, tarras79/iStock; **p. 137** Khrebtov_nika/iStock, valentinrussanov/iStock, Ridofranz/iStock, Frankhuang/iStock; **p. 142** golfcphoto/iStock, airdone/iStock, mawielobob/iStock, primeimages/iStock, Yastrebinsky/iStock, clu/iStock, andresr/iStock; **p. 143** SDI_Productions/iStock; **p. 145** PeopleImages/iStock, percds/iStock, fcafotodigital/iStock, marieclaudelemay/iStock, Ababsolutum/iStock, izusek/iStock, Elena_Rudyk/iStock, bokan76/iStock; **p. 146** KaterinaChumakova/Dreamstime; **p. 147** © Fundación Pies Descalzos; **p. 148** diane555/iStock, ArnaPhoto/iStock, TurqayMelikli/iStock, Volhah/iStock, Margolana/iStock; **p. 151** loveguli/iStock; **p. 152** Benzoix/Dreamstime; **p. 153** South_agency/iStock; **p. 154** Iefym Turkin/iStock; **p. 160** Artinspiring/

Dreamstime; **p. 162** digitalskillet/iStock; **p. 164** incomible/iStock; **p. 166** nurulanga/iStock; **p. 168** eyecrave/iStock; **p. 170** 4x6/iStock; **p. 172** Alexsalcedo/Dreamstime, Tinzabo/Dreamstime, © Fundación Niñ@s de Papel

Unidad 5 p. 174 ben-bryant/iStock, Nikita Chisnikov/Dreamstime, Ulianna19970/Dreamstime; **p. 175** Mvogel/Dreamstime, chandlervid85/AdobeStock, Baibaz/Dreamstime, Johnfoto/Dreamstime, Reporter/iStock, goir/Dreamstime, nito100/iStock, Chernetskaya/Dreamstime, Thelightwriter/Dreamstime, Floortje/iStock, Jon Helgason/Dreamstime, Tsekhmister/Dreamstime; **p. 180** JoaSouza/Dreamstime, Tuned_In/iStock, Juanmonino/iStock, elkor/iStock, Drazen_/iStock, Gang_Zhou/iStock, monkeybusinessimages/iStock, JamesBoardman/Dreamstime; **p. 183** Pablo Sebastian Guillen/Dreamstime, Pool/Getty Images, Matt Roberts/Getty Images, Harry How/Getty Images, PA Images/Alamy, KokiNagahama/Getty Images; **p. 184** TurqayMelikli/iStock; **p. 185** MarianoGarcia/Alamy, David Ramos /Getty Images, Gregory Shamus/Getty Images, Matthias Hangst/Getty Images; **p. 186** DGLimages/iStock; **p. 188** FangXiaNuo/iStock; **p. 190** Atholpady/Dreamstime; **p. 191** vasantytf/iStock; **p. 192** GoodLifeStudio/iStock, mixetto/iStock, monkeybusinessimages/iStock, Manaemedia/Dreamstime, JelenaDanilovic/iStock, SolStock/iStock, JJFarquitectos/iStock, CarmenMurillo/iStock, grinvalds/iStock, Goodboy Picture Company/iStock, andresr/iStock, sanjeri/iStock; **p. 193** S-S-S/iStock, nadia_bormotova/iStock; **p. 194** adekvat/iStock, Irina_Strelnikova/iStock, cotuvokne/iStock; **p. 195** wundervisuals/iStock, gbh007/iStock, SolStock/iStock; **p. 196** fotokostic/iStock, PheelingsMedia/iStock, hocus-focus/iStock, Baibaz/Dreamstime, skynersher/iStock, MorakotKawinchan/iStock, JJFarquitectos/iStock, sakkmesterke/iStock, isabella antonelli/iStock; **p. 198** TetraImagesLLC/Alamy, South agency/iStock, Customdesigner/iStock, Dmytro Kvasnetskyy/iStock, MarioGuti/iStock, hocus-focus/iStock; **p. 200** Aurinko/Dreamstime, bagwold/Dreamstime, Vladakela/Dreamstime, Chensen/Dreamstime, Pixelrobot/Dreamstime; **p. 201** fstop123/iStock, CASEZY/iStock, by sonmez/iStock, diego_cervo/iStock; **p. 202** VisualGeneration/Dreamstime; **p. 204** Lightcome/iStock; **p. 206** monkeybusinessimages/iStock, gorodenkoff/iStock, wundervisuals/iStock, lisegagne/iStock, Antonio_Diaz/iStock, PeopleImages/iStock, SolStock/iStock; **p. 207** SurfUpVector, Anastasiia_New, katflare/iStock; **p. 208** Yarkovoy/Dreamstime; **p. 209** nensuria/iStock, monkeybusinessimages/iStock, damircudic/iStock; **p. 210** granola/iStock, svetabelaya/iStock, OSTILL/iStock, Pool/Getty Images, Eloi_Omella/iStock

Unidad 6 p. 212 bonetta/iStock, Thelightwriter/Dreamstime, Tarzhanova/iStock, kaisphoto/iStock, LeventKonuk/iStock, Szefei/Dreamstime, AlexandraKaramysheva/Dreamstime, lena5/iStock, Antagain/iStock, Vitalily73/iStock, s-cphoto/iStock; **p. 213** SamEdwards/iStock; **p. 214** Apolobay/Dreamstime, istanbulimage/iStock, mrsiraphol/Freepik, Antagain/iStock, Raja Rc/Dreamstime, Cs333/Dreamstime, istanbulimage/iStock, bonetta/iStock; **p. 215** curtoicurto/iStock, SabrinaBracher/iStock, m-imagephotography/iStock, Staras/iStock; **p. 216** anoushkatoronto/Adobe Stock; **p. 217** Ondine32/iStock, D-keine/iStock, Dmitry Lobanov/Adobe Stock, mapodile/iStock; **p. 220** Floortje/iStock; **p. 221** Sadeugra/iStock, Kulakova/iStock, Sirfuji/iStock, ozanuysal/iStock, DeluXe-PiX/iStock, Halfpoint/iStock; **p. 222** Andreaobzerova/Dreamstime; **p. 223** Juan Carlos Tinjaca/Dreamstime, dragonimages/Dreamstime, Szefei/Dreamstime, david_franklin/Adobe Stock, Chiyacat/iStock, Aurinko/Dreamstime, GoodLifeStudio/iStock; **p. 224** Ben

Gabbe/Getty Images; **p. 226** Dtiberio/Dreamstime, Jose Antonio Sanchez Reyes/Dreamstime, kkong5/iStock; **p. 228** ManuelMedir/Getty Images, Fotoholica Press Agency/Alamy; **p. 229** monkeybusinessimages/iStock; **p. 230** Natikka/iStock, MediaProduction/iStock, kutaytanir/iStock, chictype/iStock, Tim UR/iStock, julichka/iStock, RedHelga/iStock, Studioimagen73/iStock, Sezeryadigar/iStock, SteveStone/iStock, paci77/iStock, ChViroj/iStock, kaanates/iStock, Marat Musabirov/iStock, Boonchuay1970/iStock, Alter_photo/iStock; **p. 232** onlyyouqj/Freepik; **p. 234** Valentyn75/Dreamstime; **p. 237** Pressmaster/Dreamstime; **p. 238** DronG/iStock, JosuOzkaritz/iStock, bluebird13/iStock, kajakiki/iStock, burwellphotography/iStock, terex/iStock; **p. 239** ChristianVinces/iStock, Mariha-kitchen/iStock, jmsilva/iStock, JhonTorresOspiño/Dreamstime, EdgarDPons/iStock, smpics/iStock; **p. 241** andresr/iStock; **p. 242** MychalWatts/Getty Images; **p. 244** Artofphoto/Dreamstime; **p. 245** gresei/iStock; **p. 246** fcafotodigital/iStock; **p. 247** jlo_photomaker/iStock, Christian Vinces/iStock, swetta/iStock; **p. 248** coopermoisse/iStock, asafta/iStock, Proformabooks/iStock, vainillaychile/iStock, xamtiw/iStock